Compeer

Compeer:
Recovery Through the
Healing Power of Friends

Edited by
Bernice W. Skirboll
with Lois Bennett and Mark Klemens

MELIORA PRESS

An imprint of University of Rochester Press

The publication of this volume was made possible, in part, through generous support from PAETEC Communications, Inc., Rochester, New York.

First published 2006
Meliora Press is an imprint of the
University of Rochester Press
668 Mount Hope Avenue, Rochester, NY 14620 USA
www.urpress.com

and Boydell & Brewer, Ltd.
P.O. Box 9, Woodbridge, Suffolk IP12 3DF
United Kingdom

ISBN 1–58046–232–4 (Hard back)
ISBN 1–58046–241–3 (Paperback)

Library of Congress Cataloguing-in-Publication Data

Compeer : recovery through the healing power of friends / edited by
Bernice Skirboll ; with Lois Bennett and Mark Klemens.
    p. ; cm.
Includes bibliographical references and index.
ISBN 1-58046-232-4 (hardcover : alk. paper) – ISBN 1-58046-241-3 (pbk. : alk. paper)
    1. Compeer (Organization) 2. Mentally ill–Services for–Case studies. 3. Mentally ill–
Rehabilitation–Case studies. 4. Community mental health services–Evaluation. 5. Volunteer
workers in mental health. 6. Self-help groups–Case studies. 7. Friendship.
    [DNLM: 1. Compeer (Organization) 2. Mental Disorders–rehabilitation–Personal Narratives.
3. Self-Help Groups–Personal Narratives. 4. Friends–Personal Narratives. 5. Program
Evaluation–Personal Narratives. 6. Social Support–Personal Narratives. 7. Voluntary Workers–
Personal Narratives. WM 426 C737 2006] I. Skirboll, Bernice, 1940– II. Bennett, Lois, 1949–
III. Klemens, Mark, 1956–
    RA790.5.C643 2006
    362.2–dc22   2006000205

British Library Cataloguing-in-Publication Data

A catalogue record for this book is available from the British Library

Printed in the United Sates of America.
This publication is printed on acid-free paper.

Figure 15 used by permission of the Greece *Messenger Post*.
Figure 16 used by permission of the *Providence Journal Company*.
All other photographs courtesy of Compeer, Inc.

With appreciation and love to the thousands of Compeer volunteers who have touched me by your kindness and generosity and inspired me to do all I could to build Compeer.

–B. W. S.

Contents

Illustrations

Tables

Foreword

Most people remember how they first became aware of Compeer. For me, it was in 1994, when my company attended a fundraising event in Rochester, New York, and we were quickly won over by the enthusiasm of Compeer's staff, volunteers, and board members. The more we learned about this organization, the more we realized what a great investment it would be to become involved. Over time, I was fortunate enough to be invited to join Compeer's board in Rochester, and was better able to help, both locally and through its international affiliations.

Business executives want to do what's right for their business and their employees. Compeer founder Bernice Skirboll suggests maximizing efforts by achieving multiple objectives: searching for the "Triple Play," as she calls it. Compeer provides that, as all concerned reap benefits from the friendships created. It's an enjoyable organization to be involved in and, importantly, Compeer saves communities money by providing services that otherwise might need to be supplied by state and/or local governments. From a business perspective, Compeer is a "Triple Play" model for supporting people in need.

So many times—in both the business world and in our personal lives—we look for complex solutions to problems when often the most effective answer can be found in a simple, common sense approach. Compeer keeps it simple: bring the power of friendship to those who need it. This translates across geography, race, age, and businesses. Once you learn what Compeer is all about, you can't help but get involved. For those who want to help, I consider Compeer to be the purest form of friendship to be found.

Arunas A. Chesonis, Chairman and CEO,
PAETEC Communications, Inc.,
Rochester, New York

Acknowledgments

Over the years, people often asked me what I would do when I stepped down from serving as president and executive director of Compeer. My answer was that I wanted to devote my time to writing a book about the Compeer story. Three years ago, while I was still president, the opportunity to publish a book presented itself to me. Tim Madigan, then editorial director of the University of Rochester Press, learned about Compeer through a newspaper article, and asked me to tell him more about our organization. We met and discussed Compeer's history and my ideas for a book. This project was born from that meeting. I want to thank Tim for initiating this endeavor and for his guidance in developing the structure and outline for this book.

The Compeer story is not only my story. It is made up of the memories of all our volunteers and the thousands of clients whose lives have been changed by Compeer. We wanted to include their perspectives and experiences in this book. We received an outpouring of inspiring personal narratives that touched us with their honesty and sincerity; only space limitations prohibited us from including all these wonderful pieces in the book. Thank you to all the clients and volunteers who shared their stories with us.

I am proud of Compeer's long association with the mental health profession. Many practitioners generously offered to write about their observations of Compeer. The seven clinical writers included in the book were selected, in part, because they represent a variety of mental health professions and perspectives. I am very grateful to J. Steven Lamberti, Kathleen Coyne Plum, Michele Beeley, Stephen Dvorin, John S. McIntyre, Ann McIntyre, and Richard M. Ryan for their valuable contributions. Administrators of Compeer Affiliates around the country and the world also offered to write their Compeer stories, and we selected a number of these for inclusion in the book. I thank Shannon Jaccard, Mary Thurston, Barb Mestler, Myree Harris, Michele Brown, and all the administrators who wrote to us.

I want to thank the board of directors of Compeer, Inc., all of whom supported and championed this project from the beginning. Their commitment has been outstanding and deeply gratifying. A special thank you to Arunas

Chesonis for his generosity in underwriting this book and for his ongoing support and belief in Compeer's mission.

Much of this book would still be in outline form if not for the hard work of the Compeer staff in Rochester. I am grateful to Dana Frame, Mary Ellen Budney, and Tracy Herman for writing vital chapters as well as performing other services in putting this book together, and to Andrea Shuck and Andrew Rawdon for their help and contributions. I thank Susanna Tessoni, my dedicated executive assistant for the past twenty-eight years who, despite her many ongoing responsibilities, expertly managed the requests for and the timely acquisition of all the materials and contributions for this book. I also thank Karen Wilk, Sheri Donnelly, and Catherine Giambrone who did whatever was necessary to get the book completed.

I extend a special thank you to Brian H. McCorkle, E. Sally Rogers, Erin C. Dunn, Yu Mui Wan, and Asya Lyass of Boston University and to Shannon M. Coutre and David L. Penn of the University of North Carolina for their important contributions to this book and to Compeer.

A big thank you also goes to Gene Dorsey, Dr. Alan Turow, Tim Cook, and Michele Brown for graciously reading earlier drafts of this book and for sharing their opinions and comments with me.

Every writer dreams about having a perfect editor, a partner who will guide her through all the stages of producing a book. For me that perfect partner is Mark Klemens of the University of Rochester Press. Mark's suggestions—major or minor—were always made with tact and kindness. Thank you, Mark, for all your help and advice. I also want to thank the staff of the University of Rochester Press for their efforts and dedication to this project.

I have been blessed to meet and get to know the most wonderful and generous people throughout my history with Compeer. Two years ago, I met Lois Bennett who agreed to help me with this book. Throughout this project, Lois has been my true friend. She listened to my story and captured the essence of my feelings, motivation, challenges, and historical perspective, to the point where I can start a sentence and she can finish it. I am and will be eternally grateful to Lois for donating her professional expertise. It has been a real delight to work with her.

And last but not least, a special thank you to my husband Mort for his continued support and encouragement, not only for this book, but also for my work of the past thirty years. He inspired me to run a not-for-profit organization like a business, to look at the big picture, and to focus on what's really important. Over the years, the demands of my job have forced Mort and my children Lisa and Stephen, and my granddaughters Jordyn, Rian, and Bayley to sacrifice some of their time with me, but I hope that through sharing the excitement and joy of Compeer, they gained much more in return.

Compeer works because it is a four-way partnership made up of volunteers, clients, Compeer administrators, and therapists. I wanted to thank every one of them as well as others who contributed to this project, but I might have unintentionally left someone out. If so, please forgive me and know that I really do appreciate your help and support in writing this book. I am truly grateful to all who made this book a reality.

Bernice W. Skirboll,
Rochester, New York,
March 2006

Introduction

Compeer is an award winning, not-for-profit organization that matches community volunteers in supportive friendships with children and adults who receive mental health treatment. Thousands of people and dozens of organizations have contributed to the success of Compeer, but the original ideas, energy, and impetus belong to one person: Bernice Skirboll. In this book, Ms. Skirboll discusses the events that inspired her to form Compeer, as well as her philosophy and her approach to growing an organization.

Many elements account for Compeer's successful achievements. Its programs are well constructed and tested. Its marketing plans and flair for publicity as well as its techniques for obtaining funding, client referrals, and volunteer retention are exhaustive. Its approach to volunteer training and monitoring is thoughtful and intelligent. Perhaps most important of all, Compeer staff members model enthusiasm for the organization's volunteers, and treat them with respect and gratitude. This book illuminates the services Compeer offers; discusses how Compeer works with mental health professionals, families, volunteers, and clients; explains how Compeer makes its matches and trains and monitors its volunteers; and provides additional valuable information about how to run a successful program like Compeer.

Compeer programs span the United States, Canada, and Australia. We include stories of Compeer administrators from five affiliate chapters of Compeer, who discuss their personal and unique experiences with Compeer in their communities.

Compeer has formally measured the effectiveness of its programs since 1978. In this book, we include examples of Compeer's self-evaluation process, as well as studies conducted by researchers at Boston University and the University of North Carolina at Chapel Hill, which serve to confirm that Compeer positively impacts children and adults diagnosed with mental illness. In addition, this book discusses Compeer's work in easing the financial burdens of those who are affected by mental illness, including individuals, families, and society.

Mental health professionals play an integral role at Compeer. Their essential input forms the foundation of the training, matching, and monitoring aspects of the program. In this book we include various clinical specialists' perspectives on the depth and scope of the Compeer program.

Nobody speaks more eloquently about the impact and effectiveness of Compeer than its participants: its clients and volunteers. We've included their touching and heartwarming stories about making true friendships through Compeer throughout this book. The journey of Compeer from its inception to the present has been inspirational to all and nothing short of amazing. We hope you enjoy learning about this journey and the story of Compeer.

Lois Bennett and Mark Klemens

PART I

The History, Philosophy, and Workings of Compeer

1. Compeer Through the Years

Bernice W. Skirboll, M.S.

In 1965, I was confined to bed as I recuperated from a near-fatal automobile accident. During that period, the seeds of a special community service program began to germinate in my mind. A decade later these seeds blossomed and Compeer was born. Now Compeer is an international not-for-profit volunteer organization, which successfully pursues its mission of bringing the force of friendship and mentoring support to children and adults who are in treatment for mental illness. The journey of Compeer over thirty years has been one of challenges and successes, tenacity, and ultimately exhilaration. This book goes right back to the beginning and tells the story of how a small, inpatient-friendly visiting program in a state psychiatric hospital in the 1970s, grew into an internationally recognized, model mental health organization.

I started Compeer because in the days, weeks, and months following the accident, I experienced firsthand the healing power of friendship. Ironically, the car crash occurred as I was on my way to visit a sick friend. I swerved to avoid a pothole, and collided with an oncoming car. The other driver was not seriously hurt, but my injuries included a fractured femur, crushed chest, a collapsed lung, fractured pelvis and internal bleeding. My vital signs were so bad that the surgeons postponed setting my broken leg for a full month. I was in the hospital for two months. My full recovery took more than a year.

The accident was a turning point for me. Although a fulfilling life waited for me at home, during the two months in intensive care I had ample time to think, feel, observe, and pray. I became determined to do something more with my life. I vowed that if I pulled through, I would try to make a difference to society. I was twenty-five years old, a young mother with two children under the age of three, Stephen and Lisa, and a husband who worked hard to support us all. Neither my husband Mort nor I had parents or siblings in town. We depended on friends to help with the overwhelming responsibilities involved in caring for our children and for me. Those friends became our support system.

I can't describe the sense of loss I suffered as a result of this accident, yet it was through the strength and encouragement of my friends, neighbors, and family that I recovered and regained my sense of well-being. I discovered I could endure any pain if I had loving support. Friends sent cards and visited daily with little gifts. Neighbors and new acquaintances helped me with the simple tasks we take for granted such as shampooing my hair, putting on make-up, and dressing in my own clothes instead of hospital gowns.

As I look back on that time, one friend stands out: Judy Ertischek. Although our friendship was just beginning at that time, she quickly became a person I could depend on and trust. She organized the visits and gifts. She encouraged neighborhood children to go door-to-door collecting change to buy flowers for me. After the months I spent in the hospital and at home recuperating, I began to appreciate the need we all have to connect with people who care about us. I recognized the role in the healing process of even a single friendship. Judy's faithfulness and kindness helped me understand how important true friendship is to our total health, both physical and mental.

While in the hospital I observed the other patients and noticed whether or not they received visitors. During the next ten years, while raising my children, I volunteered in their schools and at Rochester Psychiatric Center (RPC), where I worked directly with patients. Again I observed whether the psychiatric patients had visitors, and noted to my dismay that many received few if any callers. I observed, instead, patients filling their days by sitting on the wards drinking coffee, smoking cigarettes, and watching television. I noticed the emptiness of their lives. I realized there was a crucial need for human fellowship in this population, and how important it was for them to have contact with the outside world.

I decided to use what I learned about friendship and about psychiatric patients to create something that would benefit a community of people who were not as fortunate as I: people diagnosed with mental illness. Adults and children suffering from mental illness often have a hard time making and keeping friends. Family and friends often withdraw from people who have mental illness because of lack of understanding, ignorance, or shame. For some families, having a member who has mental illness is too painful. People who have mental illness experience extreme isolation and hopelessness, and feel like the loneliest people in the world.

The opportunity to fulfill my vow came in 1975. I was in graduate school at the University of Rochester, and was looking for a meaningful part-time job. I answered an advertisement, and was hired to serve as part-time director of Adopt-A-Patient, a program that served the residents of the Rochester Psychiatric Center a state facility. Adopt-A-Patient volunteers visited hospitalized mentally ill patients. The program had been founded in 1973 by the Mental Health Association of Rochester, New York.

The job appealed to me because it allowed me to use my social work background, my personal experiences, my professional education, and my extensive experience in community volunteerism including past work at the Rochester Psychiatric Center. RPC was such a compelling environment that I always felt if ever there were an opportunity to impact positively the lives of the people living there, I would seize it. During the previous year, due to changes in administration and lack of staff, the program had begun to flounder. There remained only six volunteers for 1,500 residents when I began as program director. Despite these frustrating figures, I was charged with complete responsibility for the success of the program.

We had a budget of only $3500, which originated from a grant. I immediately recognized that I had to rely on volunteers to make the program work. Even before I joined Adopt-A-Patient, I knew the importance of volunteerism, and I knew the truth of the slogan: "Never say 'just a volunteer.'" In addition to the work in my children's schools, at the Jewish Community Center, and for various women's groups, I spent a year living in a planned community in Columbia, Maryland, where I helped set up a women's resource center and a Planned Parenthood branch. During those experiences, I observed the remarkable changes volunteers could make when properly motivated, trained, supervised, and appreciated. I recognized that turning the situation around at Adopt-A-Patient would be challenging, but it *could* be done. Many of the steps that we eventually took have become lasting components of the Compeer program.

A Call to Action

I was faced with three major challenges in running Adopt-A-Patient: recruiting volunteers, gaining the support of mental health professionals, and acquiring financial resources. My first decision was to change the name of the program. In our effort to recruit more volunteers, I observed that the name Adopt-A-Patient discouraged potential volunteers who thought of "adoption" as too large a commitment. The name suggested that people who have mental problems would always be hopelessly ill. Adopt-A-Patient conveyed neither respect for the patient nor our ultimate aim: to help psychiatric patients reach their maximum level of functioning. I believed a new name could give us a new identity. I changed the name to Compeer meaning companion, equal, peer. The new name signaled a new beginning for the program.

Then, as now, Compeer volunteers are matched with individuals of the same gender who are suffering or recovering from a mental illness. The friends or "Compeers" are usually around the same age and have similar likes and interests. The exception is that clients who are minors are matched with adults, not with other children. The Compeer volunteer acts an adjunct to therapy, rather than as a paraprofessional or a pseudo-therapist. Instead, the volunteer acts as a conduit between the mental health professional and the individual while offering respite time to families. Volunteers make a commitment of four hours per month for at least one year. Many volunteers extend their commitments beyond one year and spend more time than one hour weekly with their Compeer friends.

Building a Program

I gained the support of mental health professionals by setting up one-to-one meetings at the Rochester Psychiatric Center. I made presentations to the various treatment teams and to the patients. I always asked these stakeholders what they wanted the program to accomplish. Most importantly, everyone felt invested in the program because they helped to design and develop it.

I broadened the base of referring professionals to include practitioners in all community mental health centers, family services agencies, group homes for children and adults, and those in private practice. In order to build the program, I needed to market Compeer to five distinct groups, each with a specific gap to be filled:

1. Mental health professionals: To this group, Compeer serves as an adjunct to therapy and shares the goals of recovery and support to the client.
2. Clients: Compeer can offer clients hope, reduced loneliness, friendship, acceptance, a non-judgmental friend, and someone who cares.
3. Funders: Compeer provides low cost service, can reduce hospitalization time and re-hospitalizations, and can maximize dollars available for mental health services by utilizing volunteers, our greatest resource.
4. Volunteers: Compeer offers caring individuals a meaningful, challenging volunteer experience, personal fulfillment, and an opportunity to make a positive change in another person's life.
5. Client's Family Members: Compeer extends support and respite to families, and provides a volunteer who cares about, and is trained to assist, their family member.

Identifying the five groups of stakeholders enabled us to focus our efforts on meeting critical needs.

The next problem I tackled involved the massive deinstitutionalization of patients in the late 1970s. The New York State legislature at that time began to redirect mental health funds to the community, and institutions downsized rapidly. Large numbers of recently discharged patients had to receive treatment on an outpatient basis. With thousands of people moving out of institutions and into the community, an urgent need emerged for community support services. I recognized that while a person may be diagnosed as being well enough to leave an inpatient mental health facility, he or she might not be prepared to maintain every day living skills, function independently and live in the community. To avoid the revolving door of readmission, newly mainstreamed individuals required others to show them how to meet daily challenges like shopping, riding the bus, being comfortable in social situations, and appropriately using medical and community resources. I convinced the mental health professionals who were responsible for outpatient treatment to refer their patients to us. I explained that in addition to companionship, Compeer's volunteers could provide mentoring and guidance in the daily living skills that were so critical to successful mainstreaming. Compeer volunteers would also spend leisure time with their friends, and welcome them into the community. As an adjunct to treatment, Compeer could make the critical difference in helping someone to lead a healthier, more productive life in the community.

The support of family members was secured by showing them how Compeer friends can teach everyday living skills to their loved ones. As the clients became increasingly independent, the family felt less responsible and gained more respite time. Most significantly, the family understood that someone else cared about their loved one.

Marketing Our Program

The entry point of care changed from the Rochester Psychiatric Center to our four community mental health centers during this period, so I had to "market" Compeer to the professional staff of each center. I went through a cycle of repeating the process over and over again at each center until I gained the support of the professional staff. I emphasized that Compeer was a unique community support service that could help their patients make the transition from the hospital to the community, thus reducing the need for re-hospitalization.

I also learned how to surround myself with advocates for Compeer by including political and community leaders. For example, Barber Conable, Republican United States Congressman representing our district, and then later president of the World Bank, advocated for federal funding for Compeer. To maintain the connection and to give credibility to our fundraising efforts, he was made the honorary chairman of our first fundraiser. I have maintained a long friendship with Democratic United States Congresswoman Louise Slaughter, which began twenty-five years ago, when she was a New York State assemblywoman. For organizations that depend on public funding, it is essential for credibility and recognition purposes to seek and maintain the support of both major political parties. Compeer recognizes the value of having both parties represented on our board of advisors.

With every new stage of Compeer's growth and expansion–from local, to state, and ultimately to national–I had to start the marketing and networking process all over again. During the early years, I developed my "Eight Cs of Marketing Compeer."

1. Be *creative* in discovering opportunities
2. Be *courageous* in seizing them
3. Be *collaborative* in seeing them through
4. Be *confident* in what you are doing
5. Be *committed* to making it happen
6. Be *communicative,* keeping open and flexible
7. Be *credible* in everything that you say and do, and
8. It never hurts to have a little "*chutzpah*"!

Some days I felt like all I was doing was selling, selling, selling!

I have always applied this maxim to both marketing and fundraising efforts: "If you don't ask, you don't get." Many of our employees at the Compeer offices come from a human services background, and lack sales experience. They don't think of themselves as sales people. I encourage all Compeer employees to remember they are not asking for themselves, but for our clients. It's critical to have the motivation to do this. One needs truly to have a passion for Compeer. I was always thinking about Compeer, even when I wasn't at the office!

Without a marketing budget, I needed to take advantage of no-cost or low cost opportunities to gain support and recognition for Compeer. I made use of the following resources:

- Public service announcements on TV and radio produced by the stations
- Letters to the editor, writing on various subjects including mental health, volunteerism, health care, and loneliness
- Donated advertising space in print and electronic media
- Bookmarks in libraries, book stands, and doctors' offices
- Feature stories about volunteers and clients in newspapers and on TV
- In-house publications of businesses, civic and religious organizations, and
- Speaking engagements to civic, professional and educational groups.

I recognized that although it is necessary to take advantage of every marketing opportunity, it is also important to ask for just the right amount of support. I had to be sensitive to the needs of Compeer's supporters and careful not to overstay my welcome.

I also began to recognize the importance of presenting positive stories of Compeer participants. Emphasizing the successful outcomes for people diagnosed with mental illness, by relating their recovery stories, enhanced our marketing efforts and provided Compeer with a unique opportunity to change the attitude of the public toward mental illness from one of fear to one of hope. We continue to emphasize our participants' positive experiences to this day.

Funding Our Program

Few issues are as frustrating as funding and fundraising. One of the first problems I faced when I arrived at Adopt-A-Patient Program was the lack of ongoing, dependable funding. The initial $3500 grant was due to run out within six months. The program required additional funding to continue its existence. Despite having no previous grant proposal writing experience, I systematically began to seek grants. Over the course of the next three years, I was able to secure funds from seventeen local foundations.

The first major source was the Gannett Foundation in 1976. The foundation made grants to local nonprofits in communities where the Gannett Company owned newspapers or broadcast stations. Gene Dorsey was the publisher of the Gannett newspapers in Rochester and I was able to persuade him after several visits to recommend a grant to establish Compeer locally. Later, he became the president of the foundation and encouraged continuing support of Compeer. This led to gifts from other corporations. Gene always commented on my persistence. If one approach failed to work with any of our potential funders, I would retreat, regroup, and return with a different approach on another day. Gene said he finally recommended a grant to keep me from appearing at his door again! I always did my homework and I tried to match a foundation's or corporation's goals with Compeer's needs.

In the beginning I worked with a very limited budget. Necessity required that I wear many hats. I was director, supervisor, program developer, fundraiser, grant writer, personnel manager, marketer, volunteer trainer, and match coordinator. As I searched for funding, I also reached out to various universities and colleges to provide student interns and graduate students to help us. These students became adjunct staff, and helped build the program. As I secured additional funding, I was able to add staff and grow the program.

In 1976, with the first grant, I was able to hire a secretary for ten hours per week. And as I was able to raise additional funds, we were able to add more staff such as a volunteer coordinator, a research and educational coordinator and more secretarial support. In 1978, I was able to secure enough funding to increase my own commitment to full time.

In order to insure that we had ongoing funding, we expanded our base of donors to include governmental support in addition to the support we were receiving from foundations and corporations. We applied for funding from the Monroe County Board of Mental Health, the United Way, and the New York State Office of Mental Health. While outcome studies are standard practice today, I remember an early meeting with the regional director of the New York State Office of Mental Health about potential funding for Compeer. He said I should return with documented proof of how Compeer volunteers were positively impacting the mental health system and patients' lives. I turned to the Department of Clinical Psychology at the University of Rochester. Dr. Jerid Fisher designed a series of survey questionnaires for us to assess how well we were meeting our goals and objectives. Our clients' therapists were the first to fill out the questionnaires. The therapists confirmed that volunteers did indeed make a significant impact on the lives of the mentally ill. We received our first New York State funding in 1979. Eventually, volunteers, clients, and parents were added to the evaluation process. Throughout these years, we have continued to maintain an ongoing relationship with the Departments of Psychology and Psychiatry at the University of Rochester. These relationships supplied a conduit for Compeer to professional services that a non-profit agency usually could not afford. The departments provided students and patients for Compeer and used Compeer as the subject of research.

In 1980, the New York State Office of Mental Health funded two one-day training workshops where mental health professionals from across New York State came to learn the Compeer model. Within a year, five separate groups of people expressed an interest in setting up Compeer programs in their communities. Based on the favorable response within New York State, I then applied to the National Institute of Mental Health (NIMH) for a National Program Dissemination Grant. In 1982 Compeer, Inc. was awarded a two-year program dissemination grant from NIMH. Our principal investigator was Dr. Melvin Zax, Professor of Psychology at the University of Rochester. The NIMH stated in their grant review document that they were making the award because the Compeer model possessed the following strengths:

1. Program addresses a major concern in the mental health field: the re-entry of patients into the community after a historic de-institutionalization as well as aiding socially isolated patients in the community.
2. Program is extremely well organized and conceptualized and has a flair for publicity that is an asset in this field.
3. Although Compeer directs itself towards serving the mentally ill, it is flexible enough that it can be adapted to other disabilities. In fact, many of its patients are multiply handicapped.
4. Recruitment, training, placement, and monitoring of volunteers are careful and well thought out.

5. There are hundreds of active relationships, an impressive number for this type of program.

6. Compeer has experience in program dissemination based on the New York Office of Mental Health sponsored workshops in 1980.

7. Program has generated acceptance in Rochester among public and private mental health sectors, volunteers, patients, clients, media, and funders.

8. Paid staff, although limited in number, have made excellent use of sundry community resources to support and expand Compeer's operation on both a financial and manpower level.

9. It is a well-established program that has operated for nine years and is financially stable.

10. The four-part partnership between the volunteer-client-therapist-Compeer staff is unique and provides needed support.

11. Program has received local, state, and national recognition and awards for its service from the media, professionals, voluntary and governmental sectors.

From 1982 to 1984, the NIMH provided $150,000 including scholarships to mental health professionals who wanted to start Compeer affiliate programs in their communities. Interested individuals completed questionnaires indicating why they wanted to start a Compeer program and how they would go about funding it. Compeer held two training conferences in Rochester in 1983 and 1984. As a follow-up, I traveled to the interested groups and provided on-site consultation to help them start Compeer programs in their communities.

Training Our Volunteers

We have always emphasized Compeer's dedication to the proposition that anyone who has the desire to be a friend can be a Compeer friend. To assure the referring mental health professionals that this desire was more important than the possession of a specific background or education, I needed to provide a comprehensive training program for the volunteers. To do this without a training budget, I again approached the clinical psychology department of the University of Rochester, and one of its members, Dr. Emery Cowen. He ran a community practicum program for doctoral students. With Dr. Cowan's encouragement and assistance, each year for the next five years a student elected to develop or enhance our training program. These students included Lori Jeanne Peloquin, Richard Ryan, and Jerid Fisher. Additionally, Kathleen C. Plum of the University of Rochester's nursing department developed the psychopharmacology section of the training curriculum. After designing the program, the doctoral candidates trained our volunteers, and prepared the Compeer staff and volunteers to conduct future training sessions. Our relationship with the University of Rochester paid huge dividends during this period.

Experience has borne out the principle that effectiveness as a volunteer is based on beliefs, motivation, and availability, rather than on any particular educational degree. Compeer is for everybody. Volunteers come from all walks of life, as do the clients. While volunteering for Compeer is not limited to those who have experienced mental illness, the volunteers who have experienced mental health problems bring an extra understanding and empathy to the friendship.

People often ask why Compeer works so well. I tell them that the program works because Compeer brings together strangers who might not have met through normal channels. These individuals meet through the auspices of Compeer and choose to share their time and life with a new friend. They are not family, they are not paid professionals. They are friends who have no vested interest other than to give compassionately of their time and abilities. For many individuals referred to Compeer, the Compeer friend may be the only non-paid individual in their life and their first "real" friend.

Compeer Today

Many non-profit organizations begin small, and build slowly through the years. The original premise becomes refined, and then is often abandoned for a different concept. Not so with Compeer. By necessity, Compeer experienced rapid development from the start. We required the cooperation of many individuals and organizations in order to get our program running, and so we had to succeed on many fronts—such as determining the concept of Compeer, networking, organizing, fundraising, and planning—right from day one. Thus, many of our greatest milestones occurred in the early months and years of the organization's existence.

We should not downplay, however, the astonishing growth and change that Compeer has experienced in its thirty-plus-year history. Compeer began with the basic one-to-one friendship scenario and has expanded to offer nine different programs of service to our clients. Compeer was launched in the western New York city of Rochester, and now exists in over thirty states and in three countries. At the end of this chapter, we include a timeline where you will learn about some of the accomplishments and milestones that Compeer has enjoyed over the years. We describe our various programs in more detail in chapter two. In chapter ten, we discuss the growth of Compeer around the world and share some stories from the leaders who made our expansion possible.

Current Organizational Structure

As we have noted, Compeer had local roots as a program of the Mental Health Association of Rochester, New York. After we developed a national presence, we wondered whether we should incorporate. In 1983 we formed an advisory committee to study that issue. The advisory committee decided that the organization should become independent and incorporated as Compeer, Inc. Compeer's name is registered as a service mark and we are a 501(c)(3) not-for-profit corporation. This status identifies us as a non-profit entity to which contributions are tax-deductible to the extent permitted by law. Compeer, Inc. also maintains an advisory board that consists of former chairpersons of the board of directors, former founding board members, and other people who serve in an advisory capacity.

Compeer Inc.'s board of directors meets monthly and includes an executive and numerous other subcommittees. The members of the board represent large and small corporations, financial, legal, marketing, and human resource professionals as well as volunteers and consumers. They play a leadership role in developing, growing, and governing the agency. They also make major financial contributions. Former board member Arunas Chesonis, the founder and CEO of PAETEC Communications, Inc., underwrote our annual Compeer golf tournament when it was first proposed as a new fundraiser, and PAETEC has continued to sponsor the golf outing to the present day.

Currently, Compeer programs are funded by a combination of governmental sources (state and county departments of mental health), corporations, private and public foundations, the United Way, and individual donors, as well as through fundraising events.

Organizational Entities

We have an accessible staff and an informative Web site. The Compeer staff provides community and professional education about Compeer, recruits volunteers and referrals, engages in public relations activities, organizes training, provides continuing support for volunteer/client relationships, and seeks funding for special projects and new program development.

Compeer's headquarters are located in Rochester, New York. Compeer, Inc. is comprised of three entities: the Rochester Compeer Affiliate, the New York State Compeer Programs, and Compeer International. At any given time, Compeer, Inc., employs between twenty-five and thirty employees who provide training, consultation and administrative support to more than one hundred affiliate programs located in thirty states and in Canada and Australia.

An executive director/president oversees Compeer, Inc. The following professionals report directly to this person: (1) vice president and director of the Rochester program; (2) Compeer International vice president and director; (3) New York State program director; (4) director of finances and human resources; and (5) the director of internal operations of Compeer, Inc.

The structure of the Rochester affiliate is similar to but not exactly the same as that of other affiliates. Each affiliate's structure serves the needs of its particular community. Rochester is the model program and remains the largest in the world. Reporting to the vice president and director of the Rochester program are various volunteer coordinators, a youth-parent consultant, recreation mentors, and a research assistant. The vice president/director of the Rochester program shares a research and development expert with the vice president/director of Compeer International.

One of Compeer's strengths is that it can be adapted to communities of different sizes and natures (rural, suburban, urban) and to agencies in a variety of settings. Some affiliates are part of churches or medical entities. Some fall under the umbrella of other social service agencies.

We at Compeer are proud of our many accomplishments during our more than thirty-year history, which include numerous awards and citations. We conclude this introduction to the history of Compeer with a timeline that lists our most significant achievements:

A 33-Year Timeline

1973

The Mental Health Association in Rochester, NY, establishes the Adopt-A-Patient program to enable formerly institutionalized patients to successfully live in the community.

1977

Name change of Adopt-A-Patient to Compeer
Com-peer (kom'pir) n. 1. a person of equal status or rank; a peer or equal. 2. a compare, companion, a comrade, a mate (*Webster Revised Unabridged,* 1913 Edition).

1980

New York State Office of Mental Health supports expansion of Compeer to other New York State communities. Compeer receives the Natural Support System Award (New York State Office of Mental Health).

1982

The National Institute of Mental Health awards Compeer a national Dissemination Grant.

CBS Morning News features Compeer on a program.

Compeer receives The Presidential Recognition Award from the US Department of Health and Human Services.

1983

The organization incorporates as Compeer, Inc.

At the first National Conference, eighteen Compeer programs are implemented in fifteen states.

Compeer receives the Certification of Significant Achievement Award from the American Psychiatric Association.

1984

Compeer receives the first NYS Eleanor Roosevelt Community Service Award.

President Reagan gives Compeer a Presidential Volunteer Action Award Citation.

1985

Psychology Today[1] magazine highlights Compeer for receiving the Certification of Significant Achievement from the American Psychiatric Association.

1987

Sally Jesse Raphael features Compeer on one of her television programs. Geraldo Rivera features Compeer on one of his television programs. The Compeer program expands to include at-risk youth, victims of traumatic head injury, and mentally ill homeless adults. We create "Compeer Calling."

1989

At the White House, President George H.W. Bush, presents the Presidential Volunteer Service Award to Compeer.

Newsweek runs a Special Report on Compeer, "The Power of Friendship."[2]

1991

"Family Circle" magazine features Compeer in their report on "Women Who Make a Difference: 'Friends in Deed.'"

Tom Brokaw features Compeer on his NBC Nightly News broadcast in August.

1992

Compeer establishes its first overseas program in Rotterdam, the Netherlands.

1994

Compeer establishes its Deaf and Hard of Hearing Program.

1996

Compeer establishes its first affiliate in Sydney, Australia.
Compeer publishes *Cooking with Friends International Cookbook.*

1997

Point of Light Foundation chooses Compeer as a Connect America Partner.

1998

Compeer publishes the first *Healing Power of Friends* book, a 120-page collection of volunteer and client stories.

1999

Bernice Skirboll makes a presentation at the first White House conference on mental health.
The Associated Press runs a story on Compeer entitled, "Group Helps Break Fetters of Mentally Ill" by Ben Dobbin.
Public Private Ventures, a not-for-profit organization funded by the Department of Education and Mentoring Policy Council selects this program as one of the sixteen most effective youth mentoring programs out of 700 programs nationwide.
Compeer receives the Cultural Competency Best Practices Award from Monroe County Office of Mental Health (CCSI)

2000

Compeer establishes Friends for a Day, Skillbuilders, and Recreational Mentoring Programs.

2001

Boston University Research Study begins on the efficacy of adult Compeer relationships.

2002

Compeer receives the Eli Lilly Reintegration Award for social integration
A Compeer story appears in *Chicken Soup for the Volunteer's Soul*[3]

2003

The Compeer program is presented at the World Federation of Mental Health in Melbourne, Australia
CNBC features a Compeer documentary nationally
The Associated Press runs a story on Compeer Juvenile Drug Court Mentoring Program
Congressional Record tribute to Compeer from the honorable Louise Slaughter, House of Representatives

2004

Mentoring Children of Incarcerated Parents service begins
Change in leadership in Compeer, Inc. Ben Giambrone assumes the role of president, and Bernice W. Skirboll takes on consultant role

2005

Compeer Model recognized by the American Psychological Association
Australia becomes the first country outside the United States to host International Compeer Conference
Compeer initiates Dual-Diagnosis Program

2006

Compeer: Recovery Through the Healing Power of Friends book launched in Rochester, New York in April

Notes

1. Author unknown. (1985) Me and my Compeer in "Crosstalk." *Psychology Today* 19 (1).
2. Author unknown. (July 10, 1989) Special Report. *Newsweek.*
3. Mestler, B. (2002). "The Healing Power of Friendship." In J. Canfield and M. V. Hansen (Eds.), *Chicken Soup for the Volunteer's Soul.* (pp. 281–84). Deerfield Beach, FL: Health Communications, Inc.

2. Services and Programs

Bernice W. Skirboll, M.S., Mary Ellen Budny, and Dana Frame

The numerous services and programs that are offered by Compeer are discussed in this chapter. We explain our approach to volunteer recruitment and interviewing, and how we train and supervise volunteers. We then describe procedures for making and monitoring volunteer-client matches.

We at Compeer are proud of our successes to date, and we look forward to many future achievements. Through experience we know that the foundation of Compeer's success lies in its well-constructed and time-tested procedures. Compeer provides flexible volunteer opportunities that fit every lifestyle. Although Compeer programs found around the world differ in their mix of offerings, every program is based on the same tenet: making friends can change lives.

Part I: The Services

One-to-one Friendships: Our Core Service

The centerpiece of Compeer's program is the one-to-one friendship. Research has shown that people who have mental illness strongly desire human contact and friendships. They want to be able "to go out and do 'normal' things and to [regain] parts of themselves and their lives that they had long since lost due to onset of their illness." (Davidson, 2001).[1] Friends can significantly contribute to the overall quality of life and to one's ability to cope with stress. Friendship even affects one's vulnerability to illness. (Boydell, 2002).[2]

Most volunteers choose to spend time on a regular basis—usually weekly—alone with an adult or child Compeer client. The volunteer acts as a caring, consistent, supportive friend, role model, and advocate, and becomes part of the team that includes the client and a mental health professional or therapist. Under the supervision of the staff volunteer coordinator, the volunteer chooses his particular friend based upon mutual interests, similar temperament, and other factors. We believe that everyone in our program has the right to choose his or her friends as we do in every day life. The act of choosing enables the volunteer to feel ownership and responsibility for making the relationship work. Similarly, the clients feel chosen and this raises their self-esteem.

Compeer friends share activities they both enjoy such as movies, sports, shopping, or talking over coffee. Compeer also provides many free activities for friends such as museum and theatre passes, golf tournaments, holiday parties, and special events at farms, schools, and other locations. The commitment of our organization to the training, support, and supervision of its volunteers is discussed in greater detail in Chapter 3.

Additional Services

The services of Compeer extend far beyond its centerpiece one-to-one match program. Our other services grew out of a desire to provide useful and timely programs for our referred clients. Most organizations work within the constraints of given parameters. In our case, the number of people who will volunteer at any particular time is variable, and Compeer cannot control whether these volunteers will make appropriate matches for the clients on the waiting list for a one-to-one friendship. But there are always needs to be filled, so to make sure we serve as many people as possible, we created the following ten programs:

1. Group Placements

Group volunteers interact with six to ten clients in staff-supervised settings by joining in recreational activities and outings. Typically, group settings include group homes, supervised apartments, inpatient psychiatric hospital units, and hospital psychosocial clubs.

This program is an excellent choice for our large component of college volunteers. They tend to arrive by public transportation and often travel in groups. The students can come together, do activities, and also form friendships with the clients they encounter in the facility. Groups of young volunteers can take clients out of the institution for activities or a meal. A group usually lasts for approximately one year.

2. Compeer Calling

Compeer Calling provides interim support to those waiting for a one-to-one match. Volunteers call each of several clients once a week for about fifteen minutes until the matches are made. This contact can improve the interpersonal skills of the recipient and often provides the Compeer staff with information that is useful in making appropriate matches.

We encourage our recipients to graduate from being clients to becoming volunteers in our organization. After appropriate screening and a letter from their therapists, clients usually begin their service with us as Compeer Calling volunteers. It is one thing to talk about mental illness, another thing to experience it. The Compeer graduates serve as excellent role models. Their clients think, "He did it. I can do it, too."

3. Friends for a Day

The "Friends for a Day" (FFD) Program provides a short-term volunteer opportunity at group activities for the clients. These activities may include a trip to the zoo, sporting events, a tour, or a holiday party. The volunteers undergo abbreviated training, and then accompany children and adults to these events. Compeer staff provides full on-site support. A volunteer may have a one-on-one relationship with a client or may be a friend to several clients for the day. The FFD program enables Compeer and the client to stay "connected" while they are waiting for a volunteer.

4. Recreation Mentoring Program

Once a week, the recreation mentor provides emotional or social support, companionship, guidance, and feedback in a recreational setting to a young person (between the ages of ten and sixteen years old) who has difficulty accessing and being successful in his or her community because of emotional or behavioral problems. Most often the setting is a local community center. Recreation includes, but is not limited to, board games, card games, exercises, reading, flying a kite, fishing, hiking, wall climbing, theatre, museum visiting, taking a cooking class, or anything that will help the young person engage and improve his or her social functioning.

5. Skillbuilders

Our Skillbuilders' motto is "Teach a skill, change a life." Skillbuilders is a short-term opportunity for a volunteer to teach clients a life skill. Sometimes volunteers and their "friends" participate in Skillbuilder programs together. Teachers choose to impart daily living skills like grocery shopping, handling money, proper nutrition, cooking, or computer skills. Others choose a recreational activity such as quilting, art, playing a musical instrument, or participation in a sport. The volunteer could be an artisan or a professional in the topic he or she is teaching. Most teachers are volunteers, but on occasion, some are paid for their services.

The volunteer and client meet once a week for at least one hour. Skillbuilding groups are usually made up of eight to twelve individuals. Skillbuilding programs last on the average for six weeks. In this program, clients experience increased self-confidence and self-esteem, and achieve greater independence and enjoyment of life.

One of the longest running and most successful Skillbuilding programs is the Compeer Quilting Bee in Rochester, New York. It was originally designed in 1999 to be a six-to-eight week session teaching quilting techniques, but because of its very successful outcomes, it has become a permanent Compeer program. Not only do participants learn quilting, sewing, and fabrics; they also make social connections and friendships, and gain support, which is equally important. Thirty or more women attend, on average.

In order to help with expenses, the Compeer Quilting Bee holds a quilt sale twice each year and makes some consignment quilts. The women learn business skills: pricing quilts by the amount of labor incurred, the cost of fabrics, inventory, budgeting, and marketing.

6. Juvenile Drug Court Mentoring

The Compeer Juvenile Drug Court Mentoring Program is part of a multi-faceted approach to improving the health and functioning of youth. The mentors offer and provide a unique one-to-one relationship designed to support, encourage, and guide a young person through his or her treatment and recovery while attending Monroe County Family Court Juvenile Drug Treatment Court and beyond.

The mentors are an integral part of a team that includes family, friends, service providers, and the court. The mentor helps the youth learn to take responsibility for his or her own actions and to develop positive decision-making skills. The mentors help them talk through issues, work towards goals, challenge poor decision-making, and celebrate growth. The mentors help to reconnect them to their communities by taking them to new activities and showing them how to access various resources.

7. Lunch Buddies

The concept of the Compeer Lunch Buddies program is simple: the volunteer agrees to meet a referred child for lunch once a week at the child's school. The children are selected based on at-risk factors (risk of school failure, absenteeism and truancy, troubled home life, etc.). They may or may not have a diagnosis of mental illness such as depression, conduct disorder, or ADHD, etc. Typically, we simply refer to the children as having adjustment problems. During the lunchtime visit, the Lunch Buddies can play board games, read stories, draw, do craft projects, go over schoolwork, or simply chat. The time commitment is about an hour a week for the duration of the school year.

8. Pen Pals and E-Buddies

The Compeer Pen Pals and E-Buddies programs provide the youth and adults on the Compeer waiting list with supportive written correspondence from Compeer volunteers. These programs afford the clients with the opportunity to respond and express their feelings through letters. This aids in the treatment process and lessens the severity of their emotional or behavioral disturbance.

9. Compeer R.N.

This unique program joins people with a mental health diagnosis and nursing students in a one-to-one match, but traditional roles are reversed. Clients take the role of mentor to the nursing students. The mentors teach the nursing students about living successfully in the community with a mental illness. They share their diagnoses, symptoms, recovery plan, medications, and side effects. They also discuss what it is like to be hospitalized and the stigma related to having a mental illness. In many traditional nursing programs, the mental health component involves observation in the psychiatric ward. The Compeer R.N. program presents an educational component through the eyes and experiences of people receiving services in the mental health system. The goals of Compeer R.N. are to dispel stigma, prepare nurses for community medicine, and promote the concept of recovery.

Since the Compeer R.N. program started two years ago there have been many successes. Mentor successes include the following: two mentors who became Compeer volunteers, one mentor who went back to college, one mentor who developed the courage to hold an art exhibit, and one mentor who used her volunteer experience on her resume to get a part-time job. Successes of the nursing students include two students who are working on a mental health unit, several students who have written that they are no longer afraid of being near someone with a mental illness, three students whose families were able to put to rest fears of mental illness, one student who has contacted her mentally ill mom after eight years of not talking to each other (she thought her mom was acting like this on purpose); and one student who received treatment for her teenage daughter who had been talking about suicide.

Our goal is ultimately to provide the participants in these programs with one-to-one matches if the need remains.

10. Dual-Diagnosis

This new program will serve people who are diagnosed with both a mental illness and an intellectual disability. Compeer will serve individuals as they make the transition from youth services to adult services. Intellectual disabilities include severe, chronic incapacities due to mental or physical impairment, resulting in limitations in self-care, language, learning, mobility, and economic self-sufficiency.

Part II: The Referral Process

Referral is an essential component of the Compeer program. The lifeblood of the program is the dedicated, caring community volunteer who provides friendship to people diagnosed with mental illness. For the program to thrive, the community must be aware of the breadth of its services, the flexibility of its commitment and the rewarding aspects of the Compeer volunteer experience. Mental health practitioners, most importantly, must be aware of the services Compeer provides and how those services can enhance their clients' recovery process.

People who have mental illness must also be aware of the services offered in the community so they can make choices about their treatment program. Friendships and community involvement are fulfilling and essential components to recovery. Merely making these services available would be of little use unless the people who need them know they exist. In this section, we describe the referral process.

Referrals from within the Mental Health Professional Community

Compeer depends on referrals of potential clients from various local mental health professionals. In order to obtain these referrals, Compeer contacts local mental health professionals to explain and promote the program.

Compeer's client referral base is built using a variety of sources including psychiatrists, psychologists, psychiatric social workers, psychiatric nurses, group home counselors, vocational rehabilitation counselors, recreational therapists, occupational therapists, school psychologists, and social workers. These professionals work in institutions, community agencies, or in private practice. Many treatment facilities are under contract with Compeer, and some Compeer chapters are under the umbrella of a treatment facility. Before mental health professionals contemplate referring a client to the Compeer program, we ask that they consider the following factors:

- *The client's willingness to be matched with a Compeer volunteer.* A referred individual should be informed about Compeer program guidelines before meeting a volunteer.
- *Amenability to social interaction.* The client should have a need for the kind of social interaction a volunteer friendship can provide.

- *Extent of Client's illness*. Referrals of "difficult cases" should first be discussed with a Compeer staff member to ascertain appropriateness and to determine the type of volunteer best suited for the match.
- *Disclosure of information*. Pertinent information, both psychiatric and medical, should always be disclosed. Information judged too sensitive to disclose on the referral form can be discussed with Compeer staff.
- *Completeness of Forms*. The referral forms should be filled out carefully and completely. All information requested is essential to facilitate the matching process and is, of course, confidential. The information should positively reflect the referred individual's personality, as well as demonstrate a need and desire for a volunteer. This information can enhance a client's chance of being matched.

Responsibilities of the Mental Health Professionals

We inform the mental health professional of her responsibilities as a participant in our program. The mental health professional should meet face-to-face with the Compeer volunteer who has chosen to be matched with his or her client. The mental health professional can provide valuable insight about the potential volunteer's compatibility and appropriateness. We encourage the mental health professional to discuss any questions or concerns about a volunteer with Compeer staff. If the match is deemed appropriate, the referring mental health professional and the volunteer coordinator are responsible for giving specific instructions and guidelines to the volunteer regarding the Compeer match relationship. For matches involving youth under nineteen years of age, a second meeting is required between the volunteer and the parent(s) or guardian(s) of the referred youth to discuss guidelines and to clarify the parameters of the relationship. It may be advisable for the mental health professional to be present at the meeting between the volunteer and the client's parent(s) or guardian(s).

Compeer requires that the mental health professionals monitor the Compeer relationship and report any concerns to the Compeer office. When a youth is involved, careful monitoring is particularly recommended, including periodic questioning of the youth about the type of activities engaged in with the volunteer. If the mental health professional has concerns about the appropriateness of the activities, he or she should report those concerns immediately to the Compeer office.

The volunteer and referring mental health professional should communicate with each other periodically to discuss and evaluate the progress of the relationship. Volunteers need and respect advice, guidance, and counseling that will help them act as an adjunct to treatment. A volunteer who receives periodic feedback and feels supported by the mental health professional is more apt to meet the mental health professional's goals and better serve his or her friend.

The mental health professional should report all pertinent information such as changes in the referred individual's status, change in address, and change in mental health professional to the Compeer office and volunteer.

Guidelines For Mental Health Professionals Regarding Youth Matches (ages six to eighteen)

All Compeer programs within each affiliate receive a copy of Compeer's operations manual. The manual spells out the specific responsibilities of referring therapists. Youth matches necessitate additional guidelines including the following:

- Mental health professionals should plan to work closely with the volunteer throughout the match.
- Positive reinforcement by the mental health professionals can be a helpful strategy for sustaining volunteers through difficult times.
- A meeting between the volunteer, mental health professional, and parent(s)/guardian(s) should take place *before* the volunteer meets the youth. Expectations should be shared to make sure they are realistic and appropriate.
- Parent(s)/guardian(s) should be encouraged to share any concerns with the mental health professional, Compeer program personnel, or volunteer depending upon the situation. Open communication between the volunteer and the parent(s)/guardian(s) is advised.
- Children should be questioned periodically regarding the types of activities engaged in with the volunteer. Concerns about inappropriate activities should be reported immediately to the Compeer office.
- The Compeer program staff should be notified of any changes involving the youth.

Any questions concerning procedures or specific issues, from the mental health professional, should be directed to the Compeer program coordinator of the local affiliate.

Compeer Staff Responsibilities

In every Compeer chapter and affiliate, Compeer staff members interview, screen, and train potential volunteers prior to any volunteer's meeting with the mental health professional. Compeer staff monitor the Compeer relationship and advise the mental health professional of any questions or concerns that may arise. Copies of monthly reports submitted by the volunteer to the Compeer office are sent to the referring mental health professional so the professional can keep abreast of the patient's activities. The Compeer program offers ongoing support and training for volunteers and monthly group enrichment activities for matches.

Importance of the Compeer Program

While mental illness may periodically limit the functioning of an individual, it does not limit the person's need for a sense of human connection and of personal value. A mix of negative experiences, emotional uncertainty, lack of opportunity, and social skill deficits can keep an individual from interacting assertively and successfully with others. Social isolation from the community is often a by-product of a mental illness. Without the support of a trusted friend and advocate, it is often difficult to live successfully in the community. The result of this isolation is sometimes psychiatric rehospitalization, homelessness, or even jail.

The one ingredient missing in the lives of many people who are undergoing treatment of mental illness is friendship. Compeer's mission is to provide friendships for adults and mentoring relationships for youth in order for them to move toward recovery. Compeer provides the opportunity for a trusting relationship with a caring friend. The match provides socialization activities, a caring friend and advocate, and a link to community resources.

Attracting Clients

Client participation in the Compeer program is completely voluntary. Many clients learn about the Compeer program through the mental health community, media, peer groups, as well as clients and volunteers matched in the Compeer program. Compeer clients range from three to one hundred years of age and come from all walks of life, all races, and many religions. In any given year, Compeer serves as many as six thousand individuals. People referred to Compeer reside throughout the community and generally are in one of the following levels of care: inpatient; transitional or residential living situation in a supervised facility; with family members or in a foster care setting; or an independent living situation.

A mental health professional referral is required to initiate a match. Anyone currently undergoing mental health therapy (hospital, day treatment program, mental health clinic, rehabilitation program or private practitioner) can request a referral from his or her mental health professional.

Clients and other family members often initiate the request for participation in the Compeer program, having heard about it through word-of-mouth.

Client Responsibilities and Guidelines

The volunteers in the one-to-one friendship program agree to meet with the client on a regular basis for at least one year, four hours per month. Clients must agree to this as well. Meetings should be mutually agreed upon between client, volunteer, and parent(s) or guardian(s) of youth.

Compeer relationships should not be expensive for either friend. Types of activities should be discussed between client and volunteer and, in youth matches, with the parent(s) or guardian(s). Affordability is taken into account during this discussion, as the client and volunteer are each responsible for their own expenses. Compeer programs sponsor group activities and discount tickets are available for many community events. Alcohol and non-prescription drugs cannot be part of any activity with the Compeer volunteer. The majority of Compeer clients are on psychotropic medications. The use of alcohol or non-prescription drugs sends the wrong message to clients. If the client has concerns about the volunteer or is unhappy with the Compeer relationship, they are encouraged to notify their mental health professional and Compeer program coordinator, who will help decide the future of the relationship.

The Compeer volunteer is a supportive friend but does not take the place of the client's mental health professional. Volunteers complete a monthly report that is sent to Compeer and the client's mental health professional. The report lists the time and activities shared together during the month. Volunteers are required to inform Compeer and the client's mental health professional if they have serious concerns regarding their friend's welfare.

Referral Steps: Initiating the Process

A patient may request a Compeer friend, but he or she may not initiate the referral process. The mental health professional must be an integral part of the Compeer team, and therefore initiates the referral for the patient. Compeer staff contacts mental health professionals in order to explain and promote the Compeer program. Basic criteria are provided about appropriate referrals, information on how to make a referral, and the participating mental health professional's responsibilities.

When a mental health professional determines that the potential recipient of Compeer services: (1) is clinically appropriate for the program (if a client is not at a point in his or her recovery to be able to benefit from the type of support that a friendship provides, then it probably is not the right time for the client to be involved with Compeer); (2) could benefit from the program; and (3) is interested in being referred to the Compeer program, that individual initiates the process by having the client sign a release of information form. The client then assists his mental health professional with completing a referral form. If the client is a youth, the parent, youth, and mental health professional complete the form. The Compeer staff reviews the information and determines whether or not the referred individual is appropriate for Compeer services.[3] The client is then sent a welcoming letter and a self-report form.

The Match Interview

The bulk of the match process takes place in a one-to-one meeting between the program coordinator and the volunteer. The coordinator brings information on four to six different clients to the meeting. Matches typically are the same gender with rare exceptions of young male children who would benefit from a female mentor as well. This is sometimes a necessity because of the lack of male volunteers and mentors.

Youth one-to-one matches are different from adult matches because there is an additional component in the match: the youth's family. It is important for the volunteer to recognize some of the obstacles that parent(s) and guardian(s) must overcome, in order to understand his or her role as volunteer *within the context of the family,* and to develop strategies for building a partnership with the youth's family. The volunteer will need to recognize the challenges a family with a mentally ill member must face. By providing permission for their youth to participate in the Compeer program, the family receives a period of respite. On the surface, this would seem to be a win-win situation, but parent(s) and guardian(s) may feel resentful and threatened by the volunteer's relationship with their child. The volunteer spends a relatively small portion of time with the youth participating in fun activities. Thus, without trust, openness, and flexibility on the part of the parent(s) and guardian(s) and volunteer, this can be fertile ground for divisiveness and manipulation. But early recognition of potential problems can help to prevent resentment down the road.

At this point in the process, the volunteer has determined which population he or she would like to be matched with—youth or adult. Factors that are considered in the matching interview include:

- Volunteer and client match preference including age range, challenging vs. easy match, inpatient vs. out patient, residential living, independent living situation
- Experience and maturity of volunteer
- Mutual interests of volunteer and client

- Volunteer and client time limitations and availability
- Geographic distance between volunteer and client
- Any volunteer or client transportation problems
- Professional experience of Compeer program coordinator regarding best kind of matches for volunteer.

A variety of referrals are shared with each volunteer, and the volunteer makes his or her choice. Every effort is made to find a common interest between the volunteer and the client, a starting off point. The common interest may be sports, crafts, a love of animals, or other hobbies. We at Compeer are careful to keep within the bounds of both participants' comfort levels. We consider age range, location of residence, and the activity levels of the participants. For example, if someone has difficulty walking, we would not match him with someone who enjoys a high activity level.

Confirming with the Mental Health Professional

After the volunteer selects his or her friend, the mental health professional is contacted to confirm that the individual still would like to be matched with a Compeer volunteer. The coordinator will also ask for another choice as an alternative in case the first client is not available. The program coordinator describes the volunteer to the mental health professional to assess match appropriateness and the program coordinator reviews the mental health professional's responsibilities to the match. An appointment is made for the volunteer to meet with the therapist. The coordinator should discuss pertinent questions for the volunteer to ask the therapist.

Special Factors Involving Youth

In a youth match, the volunteer also meets with the youth's parents or caregiver. During this meeting the volunteer explains to the parent or guardian his or her role as a Compeer mentor and discusses when regular visits can be scheduled. This meeting is important to build a respectful, trusting relationship between the parent(s) or caregivers and volunteer to insure a fulfilling mentor relationship.

Meeting the Friend

After meeting with the therapist and parent(s) or guardian(s), it is time for the volunteer to meet with his or her friend. This protocol is followed because if any concerns arise after meeting the therapist and parent(s) or guardian(s), the Compeer friend is not disappointed if the match is not made. People with mental health disabilities often have had many disappointments in their lives so every precaution is taken so that an adverse match process does not have a negative impact on the client.

The first meeting between volunteer and friend involves getting to know one another, setting and discussing expectations for the friendship, considering how time together will be scheduled, and discussing the types of activities that are affordable for the volunteer and the friend. When the volunteer and the friend have met and feel comfortable about continuing to meet, the volunteer notifies the program coordinator that the friendship is ready to be activated into the program.

Match Activation

The volunteer initiates the first regular contact with his or her new friend. This can be done by phone, after the volunteer has notified the mental health professional and parent(s) or guardian(s) that they will be calling their friend. Alternatively, a meeting can be arranged with the Compeer coordinator, volunteer, and friend. During this contact, the volunteer and friend discuss the nature of the friendship role, begin the process of getting to know each other, start building trust, begin finding common interests and experiences, set up expectations and limitations, establish a routine for contacts and assessing one another's likes and needs.

Although the primary function of the match is friendship and socialization, once a positive relationship is established, it is possible to begin working toward more specific goals. Compeer is not a treatment intervention, but it can provide assistance and problem-solving strategies within the context of positive, normalizing social interaction, which enables the Compeer friend to become more independent, capable, and involved in the community. During the one-year period, the friend may choose one or two specific goals, with input from his or her mental health professional that he or she would like to work toward within the Compeer relationship. In a Compeer friendship, participants strive to reach goals such as practicing and enhancing socialization skills, decreasing isolation and loneliness, accessing community venues, and increasing self esteem and self confidence. Some of the match activities relate to such goals, while others are designed to meet the primary social function of the match. Most activities involve just the volunteer and friend within a community setting, but Compeer also provides a number of activities and get-togethers for all matches to attend.

Monitoring and Supporting Active Volunteers

Compeer program coordinators contact new volunteers within one week of the match activation to find out how the first meeting went. The coordinator asks if the volunteer has any follow-up questions. It is the job of the coordinator to make the volunteers feel supported. The program coordinator on a monthly basis monitors youth matches by contacting the volunteer and the parent(s) or guardian(s) of the youth for the first three months. Any concerns regarding the volunteer are discussed with the Compeer program coordinator.

All volunteers are required to submit monthly reports to the program coordinator in writing, by fax, over the phone, or by e-mail. The monthly reports contain information regarding the time the volunteer has spent with his or her friend, the activities participated in during the month as well as an opportunity to state any concerns the volunteer may have regarding the relationship. Volunteers are encouraged to contact their program coordinator directly if any questions, concerns, or challenges arise in the relationship.

Support meetings for Compeer volunteers offer opportunities for information, discussion, additional training, problem solving, and for sharing ideas and resources. A Compeer newsletter provides information about activities, matches, new participants, training sessions, support meetings, and program progress. A volunteer recognition ceremony is conducted once each year.

Match Termination

As the volunteer approaches the end of the one-year commitment, he or she must decide whether to continue or end his or her Compeer relationship. Factors that influence the decision include the success of the relationship and the time availability of the volunteer. It is important for the volunteer to contact the program coordinator as soon as this decision is made. For most people, ending a relationship, whether it was a good or bad one, is a difficult process. For people in the Compeer program, many of whom already feel vulnerable, not having an opportunity to formally end the relationship can be devastating. That is why a well planned and a positive "good bye" is so important.

Two-thirds of the volunteers continue their match past the year mark. By that time a friendship has formed that may continue for years. Some volunteers encourage their clients to become volunteers themselves. As noted earlier, Compeer Calling is a great starting point for first time client-volunteers.

Summary

Compeer provides an array of services that vary from affiliate to affiliate. Every Compeer affiliate, however, offers the core one-to-one friendship program. Our clients enter the system through referrals from their psychotherapists who have determined that Compeer is appropriate at this stage of recovery. Potential volunteers are carefully screened and then matched with a client with whom they have much in common. The match is monitored and supported by the referring mental health professional and the Compeer volunteer coordinator for the length of its existence, typically for at least one year. In the next chapter we discuss volunteer recruitment, screening, and training in greater detail.

Notes

1. Davidson, L., Haglund, K. E., Stayner, D. A., Rakfeldt, J., Chinman, M. J., Tebes, J. K. (2001) "It was just realizing . . . that life isn't one big horror": A Qualitative Study of Supported Socialization. *Psychiatric Rehabilitation Journal, 24 (3)* 290–91.

2. Boydell, K. M., Gladstone, B. M., Crawford, The Dialectic of Friendship for People with Psychiatric Disabilities in *The Psychiatric Rehabilitation Journal* (2002) 26 (2) 129.

3. Boydell, K. M., Gladstone, B. M., Crawford, The Dialectic of Friendship for People with Psychiatric Disabilities The *Psychiatric Rehabilitation Journal* (2002) 26 (2) 129.

3. Volunteers

Bernice W. Skirboll, M.S., Mary Ellen Budny, and Dana Frame

The volunteer is Compeer's most important asset. Without our volunteers, there would be no Compeer program. *Every* volunteer is important. When the needs of our volunteers are met, everyone benefits: our clients, the mental health professionals, and the program.

The Compeer volunteer is an adult who generally gives a minimum of four hours each month to build a friendship with someone in need. Our volunteers are representative of all segments of society. They may be college students, community leaders, retirees, teachers, businessmen and women, or clergy. But they each share a passion for service, and for advancing Compeer's mission of healing through the power of friendship.

Compeer volunteers are not paid, so it is essential to have an aggressive, well-conceived marketing plan in order to obtain an ongoing stream of volunteers. Recruitment is a year-round activity. We emphasize that volunteer opportunities are not limited to the one-to-one match. Many volunteers enjoy involvement in other areas of the program such as office, clerical, fund raising, training, client enrichment, public speaking, committees, and board participation.

Compeer has put elements in place to ensure that each volunteer who is going into a one-to-one match is prepared and motivated for this special relationship. The "formula" for ensuring a high quality, motivated volunteer includes recruitment, training, supervision, and recognition. Each of these elements of the volunteer preparation process is described in the following pages.

Recruitment

Volunteers are recruited in many ways including through presentations to local civic and professional groups; through the media, including radio, television, newspapers and internet; and when existing volunteers recruit friends and business contacts.

We truly believe that the best way to attract volunteers is through the word-of-mouth recommendations of current and past volunteers. Who can better convey the value of volunteering at Compeer than somebody who has been there and who is respected for his contribution? Our volunteers can present specific examples of the results of their efforts. By sharing their own personal experiences, joys, rewards and challenges, volunteers motivate and encourage other people to seize the same opportunity. By using our present volunteers as spokespeople, we attract new volunteers.

Sheriff Andrew P. Meloni of Monroe County, New York, began his involvement with Compeer as a one-to-one volunteer in 1986. His public visibility was a major asset to our organization when he later served as spokesperson for Compeer, and played an active role in the recruitment of new volunteers. All of our volunteers become ambassadors for Compeer. Their enthusiasm for our programs, like that of Sheriff Meloni, helps to spread the word.

Explaining the Volunteer's Role

Under the Compeer recruitment plan, detailed information is provided to potential volunteers so they can make an informed decision about volunteering. Compeer presents information about its history, credibility in the mental health community, flexibility, range of volunteer opportunities, and the unique chance to make a difference in someone's life. Futher, we discuss the role that a potential volunteer will be asked to fill. The Compeer volunteer is not a social worker, mental health professional, or chauffeur. The role of the volunteer is to be a friend. It is more than enough to be a friend, in fact. Thoreau said, "The most I can do for my friend is to simply be his friend," a sentiment we wholeheartedly endorse!

Each Compeer volunteer is considered for a one-to-one friendship or group relationship with several persons diagnosed with mental illness. After being carefully screened by the Compeer staff and referring therapist, as described in the previous chapter and more fully below, the volunteer is matched with an appropriate individual of his or her choice. The volunteer assists with and enhances the successful rehabilitation and re-entry of the Compeer friend into the community by providing individual support. Compeer's goal is to complement professional care by providing a meaningful friendship and role model outside the traditional mental health setting. Persons may attain a higher level of functioning by improving their communications and social skills, by achieving a sense of security and belonging, and by increasing their self-esteem, and interpersonal trust. The volunteer may also advocate for his or her Compeer friend in obtaining more appropriate levels of housing and investigating community resources, education, and work opportunities.

The volunteer must attend all training sessions, undergo a background check, submit monthly reports to the Compeer office, and meet with his or her friend for a minimum of four hours per month. The volunteer is responsible for advising the Compeer staff and for referring any questions or concerns associated with the match to the Compeer staff or the therapist.

Interviewing and Screening Prospective Volunteers

A screening interview is scheduled between the prospective volunteer and a Compeer program coordinator. Each potential volunteer completes a volunteer application form and a reference form prior to the interview. If a potential volunteer has received medical or psychological treatment within the last year, a release of information form must be submitted to Compeer, so that staff can obtain permission to contact the mental health professional regarding recent medical or psychological treatment and how that may affect the volunteer's commitment. We try to ascertain whether this program is appropriate for the volunteer, and whether he will be dependable and committed to the program. We are interested in the welfare of both our clients and our volunteers.

A Compeer program coordinator's initial interview with the volunteer typically takes place at the Compeer office. The initial interview generally lasts for an hour.

Screening is an important part of every interview. Program coordinators are trained in interview skills that help them to get to know the applicant: their likes, dislikes, opinions, knowledge, and attitude towards mental health issues. Interviewers also look for any red flags that could signal an inappropriate volunteer. All potential volunteers are asked to sign a volunteer clearance form that gives Compeer permission to conduct a criminal records check and verify information regarding criminal records or pending charges, license suspension, and other information. A volunteer who drives must also provide a copy of his or her license and insurance declaration page.

Compeer requests information about a potential volunteer's preferences concerning age, religion, and ethnic background. The potential volunteer is told several times during the interview and matching procedures that sensitive questions are asked in order to increase the probability of a successful match. These sensitive questions concern sexual orientation and experience with mental illness. We ask about personal, family, and friends' histories of mental illness.

Placement can be found for nearly every volunteer, given the variety of opportunities. Volunteers are utilized in such programs as one-to-one matches for youth and adults; Compeer Calling; Skillbuilders; Friends for a Day; Pen Pals; E-Buddies, and group opportunities. If a potential volunteer is inappropriate for a Compeer placement, he or she might be redirected to a more appropriate agency. No final decision concerning a volunteer's appropriateness is made before all paperwork has been completed and thoroughly reviewed.

The Training Process

After the interview has been completed, the potential volunteer is scheduled for a formal training session. Training occurs almost immediately so that the volunteer may maintain an ongoing association with Compeer and strengthen his or her personal commitment to the organization.

The information that is gleaned about an applicant during training–as well as the interview, references, criminal records check, and the person's ability to provide personal support to a Compeer client applicant–is crucial in determining appropriateness for an experience with Compeer. The applicants who are chosen to volunteer for Compeer share the following traits: reliability, dependability, patience, and open-mindedness.

We notify the applicants of our decision personally, usually by phone, and as soon as references are checked and all the background information is received.

Volunteer Training

Volunteer training is designed to communicate to prospective volunteers the guidelines and expectations of the Compeer program, and to prepare them to function effectively in their roles as volunteers. During the training, volunteers are introduced to Compeer's history, resources, and processes. The training program educates volunteers about mental illnesses, provides details regarding the role of the volunteer, and promotes discussion of challenging issues and situations that might arise during the course of involvement with a Compeer match.

Volunteers are given a history of Compeer's origination in Rochester, New York, in order to understand Compeer's mission, its vision, and the historical journey the program has traveled over three decades of vast societal changes. Public perception of mental illness, along with advances in medications, evolution of treatment program designs, prioritization of government funding, and the changing roles of HMOs and health insurance benefits have all had a significant impact on people with mental health disabilities. Volunteers learn how these changes impact their matches.

Volunteers are educated about the Compeer process, which details the steps involved in becoming a volunteer and the amount of time from interview to the meeting with their match. The volunteer preparation process includes an initial interview with a Compeer program coordinator; training; the match interview; a meeting with a mental health professional; a meeting with parent(s) or guardians of youth (in youth matches); and finally meeting the new Compeer friend. Throughout this process, the potential volunteer is contacted and updated on the progress of the matching procedure by the program coordinator via phone and email.

The length of the volunteer preparation process varies depending on the availability of the volunteer's references, the outcomes of screening, the availability of therapist times, and the availability of the volunteers for meetings. The average process length is four to five weeks.

A basic knowledge of mental health issues is important when working with the population that is our client base. Each volunteer is introduced to a glossary of mental illness categories that includes: Affective disorders (also known as mood disorders); schizophrenic disorders and anxiety disorders. Basic facts about various mental illnesses are presented to volunteers, as well as the role of psychopharmacology in mental health treatment.

Volunteers are equipped with a summary of responsibilities and with guidelines for a Compeer relationship. The training session addresses each volunteer's responsibility in detail. Volunteer responsibilities include maintaining consistent, in-person contact with the match; contact with the mental health professional and Compeer staff as needed; completion and submission of monthly updates to Compeer; completion of annual satisfaction survey; maintaining confidentiality and handling crisis situations involving abuse or potential suicidality. A volunteer must also be familiar with the steps involved in ending a relationship.

Volunteer guidelines discussed in training include the importance of the mutual choice of social activities, travel tips, expectations for the Compeer relationship, the importance of building a trusting relationship, tips of effective communication, negotiation of boundaries in the friendship, examples of inappropriate behavior a client may display due to a lack of experience in unfamiliar social settings, how to combat stigma, and examples of methods which can facilitate a client's ability to advocate for himself or herself. Potential volunteers are provided with an array of possible questions to ask the mental health professional at the introductory meeting. In the case of youth matches, possible questions that the parent(s) and guardian(s) may have are also discussed. There are three pre-match activation training sessions and one group, post-match activation training session. Some of the pre-match training takes place at the screening interview and at the appointment with the therapist.

Upon the completion of training, each potential volunteer is given a packet of information, which includes the volunteer handbook, the name of their Compeer program coordinator with contact information, a Compeer volunteer training completion card, a list of suggested activities, and informational resources and websites.

Compeer's training program is reviewed and updated on an ongoing basis. The goals of the training are to educate and prepare volunteers to function effectively in their roles. Volunteers are also required to attend a group discussion session to share concerns and receive support at some point within the first three months of their match.

Pending Status

After the training session, the potential volunteer enters a period referred to as "pending status," or the time between interview and activation. Staff support is crucial at this point to ensure volunteer commitment and motivation. Compeer staff will contact the new volunteer and referring mental health professional on a weekly basis to update him/her on the matching progress.

Supervision

As part of the training session, Compeer staff will teach volunteers how to fill out and submit monthly reports. Compeer keeps track of the number of visits and hours spent with clients as well as success stories and problems. Sometimes our matches have difficulties with communication, with feeling comfortable with the new volunteer, and with understanding the role of the volunteer. The program coordinator provides ongoing support and guidance to the matches. After the coordinator reviews the information in the monthly report, he or she will contact the volunteer or therapist if follow-up is necessary.

Recognition

Each volunteer is recognized for his or her commitment and caring in many formal and informal ways. Informal recognition can mean telephone calls, notes, or pats on the back. Annually, Compeer volunteers are honored at formal recognition events that include special awards for outstanding volunteers and outstanding youth match of the year.

Youth Matches

Youth matches have different dynamics than adult matches, and these differences must be communicated to potential youth volunteers. Young people in the formative years of their lives should develop resiliency through positive relationships. Young people who feel isolated, lonely, have few social supports, and who experience poor academic performance in school are at risk for developing serious behavioral or mental disorders. Those who already have a mental health diagnosis may be seeking acceptance in society. A mentor relationship can build resiliency through the knowledge that someone cares without expecting anything in return. And participation in activities can help the youth to feel connected. Additionally, the volunteer will have to develop a positive and trusted relationship with the youth's parent or caretaker through good communication strategies, such as supplying regular updates.

Compeer provides mentors and friends with continued support through networking opportunities such as workshops, meetings, and activities. The program coordinator is always available to support the volunteer.

Why Volunteers Like Compeer

Unlike most volunteer work, the Compeer experience allows one person to have a direct impact on the life of another. The depth and quality of training and level of support from the program coordinator and mental health professional provide the volunteers with the tools they need for their special friendship. At Compeer, volunteers are confident that they make an important contribution, whether they are visiting their clients for just one hour a week or whether they are taking on additional responsibilities like board membership.

Compeer volunteers value the scheduling flexibility of their program commitment. Volunteers can meet with their friends at mutually convenient times to participate in activities of common interest. They appreciate the freedom to choose the client with whom they think they will be comfortable working, a choice based on common interests, location, and other criteria. The sheer simplicity of "just being a friend" encourages volunteers to initiate a Compeer relationship. The specific time commitment of four hours a month is appealing. Approximately two-thirds of volunteers stay beyond their initial one-year commitment.

Our volunteers receive direct personal benefits from their experience with Compeer. According to Christopher Peterson, professor of psychology at the University of Michigan, "When you're volunteering, you're distracting yourself from your own existence, and that's beneficial. More fuzzily, giving puts meaning into your life. You have a sense of purpose because you matter to someone else." (Wallace, 2005)

In the 2004 survey results from Rochester, New York, our volunteers had the following to say:

"I'm proud to be a part of Compeer."

"Compeer is a wonderfully rewarding experience."

"Compeer is truly there for people with mental illness."

"Compeer seems tight run and very professional. They have many suggestions for activities and maintain contact with volunteers."

"Compeer does such a creative, enthusiastic, professional job in promoting relationships. It's what the whole world needs, not just the mentally ill."

"I feel very supported by the organization. All of my questions have always been answered and I feel that the organization strives to provide and create wonderful opportunities for both volunteers and clients."

"I no longer feel like a volunteer, but a friend."

Summary

Compeer recognizes the importance of our volunteers and values their contributions. Through our marketing and recruitment strategies we make every effort to reach all potential volunteers for Compeer. We employ a comprehensive screening and training process in order to insure that we have the most qualified and prepared volunteers for our programs. Training is ongoing, as is the monitoring and supervision of the matches. Our volunteers give a great deal of themselves, and we strive to reward their efforts both informally and publicly.

Reference

Wallis, C. (January 17, 2005). The New Science of Happiness. *Time*.

4. Stories

Helping Molly Grow

Alice O'Dwyer

We met for the first time thirteen years ago, and we've been meeting ever since! Initially I wondered, could a retired teacher and an eight-year old little girl form a new and lasting friendship? I guess the answer to my question is a resounding "Yes!" Compeer has provided us with the opportunity to create an enduring relationship, and this bond has touched both our lives in a meaningful and positive way.

It all began in the fall of 1991. I was a newly retired elementary teacher, and my Compeer match, "Molly" (not her real name), was a second grade student at School #12 in the city of Rochester. We both entered this new commitment eagerly but certainly from different perspectives. Having experienced some emotional trauma, Molly was in need of someone who could help her heal and restore her damaged self-esteem. I, on the other hand, was looking forward to working on a one-on-one basis with a young girl and hoping that I could help her with her problems.

During Molly's elementary school years, we met each week. I would often pick her up at school, and we would spend the afternoon participating in a variety of activities. Molly looked forward to our get-togethers, and we always had a lot of fun. Our outing became a special afternoon in her weekly schedule. It was a treat and diversion for her to get out of her home and have something to do.

Molly's home was extremely busy and often very noisy. Molly lived with her mom and two of her three siblings. In fact, the first day I met Molly one of her older sisters was moving back into the house with her two young children. The house was crowded and always filled with many people. It seemed to be the neighborhood gathering spot, and there was always the frenzy of loud music and loud conversations. In her home environment, it was difficult for Molly to have anyone's individual attention. Thus, our weekly afternoon excursions gave Molly the chance to have my undivided focus.

I too looked forward to our get-togethers. I loved being with Molly and taking her to feed the ducks, visit the pumpkin farm, walk through the apple farm, see the animals at Lollypop Farm, etc. As we got to know each other better, I felt that Molly understood that I was someone who encouraged and supported her and that she was able to trust me. She knew she could count on me to be there for her each week.

Sometimes I would ask Molly to invite a friend to come along with us. For instance, Molly loved to go roller-skating at an indoor rink. (While I was up to doing most things with Molly; rollers skating was not one of them!) So, it was more fun for Molly to have a friend join her on the rink. Every now and then Molly would bring a friend along, because it was obvious to me that Molly needed time to socialize with her friends.

School was not a high priority for Molly. During her elementary years, she moved three times, and each new address entailed attending a new school. Being an educator, I became quite frustrated that I couldn't motivate her in this area. Her teachers were very concerned about her academic achievement and truancy. Although we worked on her assignments and projects when we were together, there didn't seem to be any follow-through on Molly's part. It was hard for me to accept her behavior. I became very disappointed when Molly did not perform well in school. However, during this period, it was important for me to remind myself of the parameters of my Compeer commitment. I had to remember that I was in the relationship to provide patience, reassurance, and support. As her Compeer friend, I was not her parent or teacher.

By the time Molly was in high school, she was attending an alternative BOCES program in Rush. This program incorporated many "hands on" activities in the curriculum. For a time Molly seemed to be doing well in this school. However, a problem with one of the bus drivers caused Molly to refuse to return to the school. When that occurred, plans were made for Molly to return to her public high school in Brockport and complete her education there. Those plans, however, were terminated when Molly became pregnant. We realized that her graduation from high school was not going to become a reality.

Molly was excited about becoming a mom and looked forward to the arrival of her baby. Although I was very surprised by the news, I realized that as her Compeer friend, I had a definite role to play during the time of her pregnancy. I immediately headed to Barnes and Noble to purchase pregnancy and "how to" baby books. Soon Molly was armed with all the information she would ever need about motherhood. With a positive attitude, I joined her in looking forward to the birth of her child. It was important that I continued to show Molly my complete support.

From the moment Molly's daughter was born, parenthood seemed to come naturally to Molly. Although she was so young to have a child, she took on her new role with tremendous maturity. She has been such a patient and loving mother. I think the most amazing part of Molly's new and demanding responsibility was that she never got upset or frustrated by the infringement of time that a newborn requires. I have been proud of Molly's ability to meet the many requirements of motherhood in such a relaxed and mature manner. I was honored when Molly's daughter was given my name for her middle name and when my husband and I were asked to be her godparents.

Over time, any friendship you share with someone undergoes change. It goes through various transformations due to the vicissitudes of life. This was obviously the case with my relationship with Molly. I can't pinpoint exactly when the transformation happened. It was the same transition parents experience when their children reach adulthood. All of a sudden your child has grown up and matured right before your eyes! Now Molly and I were no longer concentrating on her high school situation; but instead, our attention was primarily focused on her new role as a mom. She was certainly thrust into adulthood earlier than most people; nevertheless, it caused us to bond at a new level. Now both of us were parents, and both of us were moms. I could share my parenting experiences with her, and I was flattered when Molly asked my advice concerning some of the problematic situations that arise with childrearing.

My role as a mentor has continued over the years. After Molly's daughter was born, we naturally devoted our attention to that new responsibility. I did not, however, forget that Molly had been unable to graduate from high school. I realized that it would be very important for her to achieve that goal. As her advocate, I contacted various people in the educational field to see if she could possibly attend classes in order to take the GED exam. Initially, we could not get very much cooperation. We needed to have two things happen: childcare for her daughter and transportation to and from school. With perseverance and many, many, phone calls, we finally made it happen. We were so happy that everything fell into place! To make a long story short, Molly passed the exam, and we celebrated with a graduation party for her and her whole family! It was such a wonderful celebration!

Now that Molly's daughter is in kindergarten, we are looking to the future for Molly's education and career plans. At the present time, we are investigating the curriculum at Monroe Community College. We are very hopeful that we can take the next step so that Molly can receive the education she needs in order to find employment in her career choice. I am very confident that Molly will be very successful in whatever field she selects for her future career. As her friend, I plan to help her, starting with the admissions process all the way to graduation! We're certain to have another great reason for a celebration!

So, I hope this short story about Molly and myself gives a good indication of what is involved in a Compeer match. It involves a friendship that can restore hope and joy into a person's life. The knowledge that someone truly cares about you can bring significant healing. Friendship builds self-esteem and trust. For Molly, I feel I entered her life at a point where she benefited from such a relationship. I became someone she could always contact no matter what was going on in her life. She knew that I would be there for her and that I would always try to encourage her in a positive way.

I too have greatly benefited from my friendship with Molly and my Compeer commitment. It has given me a much better understanding of mental illness and emotional problems. It has educated me in the field of mental illness and has enabled me to better understand all the facets of the disease. My contact with Molly over the past thirteen years has also allowed me to get to know her family very well. In that capacity, I have learned to better understand the multitude of problems that some families face on a daily basis. It has taught me to be non-judgmental and to appreciate all the qualities within a person that deserve sincere praise. Compeer has made me realize how important it is to applaud each person for the outstanding gifts they have to offer to the world. I have often commented that I believe one of life's greatest joys is to feel, in some small way, that you have positively affected the life of a child. I hope that I have been successful in that endeavor through my affiliation with Compeer. I feel privileged to be a part of the organization.

Blind Friendship

Michelle McCumbers

I was really looking forward to spending the holidays alone like I always do. One of the things I enjoy most is hunting for recipes. I was thinking of celebrating Christmas with a roasted chicken and herbed potatoes, along with a glass of wine, maybe two. But that wasn't going to happen this year. My Compeer mentor and new friend, Joy, called me last night to ask if I would spend Christmas with her and her family tomorrow. They were having it at her daughter's house. When she asked, I immediately back peddled. I rambled off the many excuses I've used in the past to avoid social situations, "Oh, I'm not sure if I'll be able to make it. How many people did you say would be there?" By the time I hung up I found myself saying, "I'll be there by two." Then those feelings started to creep in. I don't really know these people. I won't fit in and once again I'll be alone in a crowded room.

You see, I have never actually met Joy, but I've known her for two years. We became friends through Compeer and only spoke over the telephone. At this point in my life I wasn't ready to breach my protective and comfortable barrier of shyness, so it was easier to keep in touch by phone and that was fine by me. When I got used to talking to a complete stranger, we began to talk a lot. She told me about how beautiful Arizona was when she lived there and how much she'd like to go back. I told her about my dreams and my hopes to pursue them. Joy was willing to listen to me and suggest ways of reaching my goals. She was much older than I, and had many life experiences.

In her scratchy but self-assured voice she described herself as having an olive complexion, petite body, long blonde hair, very Italian, and blind. *Blind?* It's easy to forget something like that while you're talking to her over the phone. She works as a paralegal and is a strong advocate for people with disabilities. She's not afraid of anyone or anything. She would get in your face if that were what was needed to get the job done. The only thing I was afraid of was the other people who would be there, not to mention the children. I was looking forward to tasting her much lauded lasagna that she said she would be cooking. Joy was the only one I would know there, so that would make Christmas more bearable.

I phoned Joy on Christmas Day to tell her that I'd be there in forty minutes. Of course I got lost. To make things worse I was an hour late and everybody was waiting for me. I felt like turning around and feigning illness, but I've cancelled our meeting in the past and could not do so now. A screaming child answered the door. Joy came over and hugged me and turned to lead me into the kitchen. I sat next to her while she lit a cigarette and introduced me to her daughters. Everyone went about their business, preparing food and setting the table for this day's ritual.

Exhaling a breath of smoke, she told me how good it was to finally meet me. I looked her in the face and returned the greeting. Her head barely moved as her eyes zeroed in on my face. One of her eyes was a milky blue and the other large and dark. I caught myself staring. She just stared blankly back with a haze of smoke around her head. I was starting to feel out of place. Not just because I didn't know anyone here, but because I was the only one that noticed that Joy was blind. Joy isn't helpless, that's for sure, although I felt like it. I watched her feel around for her soda, not sure if I should tell her, "A little to the left." For a moment I was startled, it seemed like she could really see me, and then I wasn't sure where I was supposed to look.

She continued chatting with her daughters while I cringed among what seemed like normal chaos for them. As I sat there I tried to imagine what it would take to survive losing your eyesight. Courage . . . it would take a lot of courage. The courage to stumble into things. The courage to remember the layout of a room, or to remember a phone number, because you can't just write it down. The courage to cross a busy street, because the bus passes you knowing that you couldn't see him. The courage to depend on other people to help you with the mundane things, like reading mail.

As it is I can see, and I am still unsure of myself; how could I survive being blind? I have to sleep with the light on, because it's frightening to wake up from a bad dream in total darkness. For me, being blind would be like trying to find the light switch when there was none, before the boogeyman got you. I always catch myself saying things like, "Did you see . . ." this or that?" I found that it was difficult to describe the intensity of a sunset or the arrangement of a painting. I'm learning that her world is not only about the other senses, but a world of words and imagination, so instead of wishing that I could show her something I'm honing my skills to describe it to her.

Christmas dinner was very good, and we all sat around talking while the children played with their new toys, not so quietly. When we were finished, Joy invited me to see her apartment. I followed while a friend dropped her off in the parking lot. Joy was ambling towards the apartment building's entrance when I caught up to her. She stopped and took out a white twelve-inch stick and threw her arm forward like a magician, and just like magic the stick extended four feet. She waved it in front of her and side to side trying to sense her surroundings and nearly hit me with it. I forgot that I needed to tell her where I was. We went into her apartment and she showed me her collection of clowns by name and location. There must have been at least a hundred clowns. I didn't have the heart to tell her that clowns frightened me. After that we talked for a while and had some coffee. She asked what time it was. It was late. I looked down at my watch but before I could tell her, I heard a beep and a harsh electronic voice say, "The time is 11 P.M." The watch she was wearing spoke the time. Before I left, Joy told me that she would be getting a seeing-eye dog next month. She said it would give her more freedom.

Driving home I thought about meeting Joy for the first time. I had never met anyone who was visually impaired before. I realized that night that I was the one who was blind. I was the one with outstretched arms feeling my way around someone who was perfectly comfortable in her own environment. Since my relationship began with my Compeer mentor, I have become more confident in myself and I am on the path to fulfilling my goals. With the support of my Compeer mentor I have completed and graduated from the Small Business Management course at Mohawk Valley Community College. I participated in a commercial for Compeer of the Mohawk Valley, Inc. I was interviewed for a local news channel that focused on the benefits of mentoring. With Compeer, I have made a friend and it has changed my life.

Friends For Life

Sara Hughes

Over the last five years, Compeer has given me the opportunity to form a very special friendship with a young person. This relationship has significantly influenced many of my life choices and goals. When I first met "Monica" in 1999, she was a shy eleven-year-old. By all outward appearances, we had little in common besides our gender. Neither of us would have imagined then how much our meeting and subsequent friendship would change us both.

I had just returned to college after marrying and starting a family. I had a lot on my plate between school, home, and part-time work as a server in a local restaurant, but I felt a strong urge to become involved in the community, too. I did some research and chose to find out more about Compeer because I found the concept of utilizing friendship to ease the pain and loneliness of individuals with mental health issues extremely compelling. After talking with one of the volunteer coordinators, I decided to commit to volunteering with a young person in the program.

A short time later, I had completed the interview, screening, and training process and was ready to choose the youth I would mentor. I heard descriptions of a few girls and then we got to Monica. I don't know exactly what it was, but something about the details of this young girl's circumstances really struck a chord with me. I let the coordinator know and, with her help, I scheduled a meeting with Monica's therapist and guardian.

Meeting the therapist was very helpful because I got to ask questions about recent developments in Monica's life, what her challenges and strengths were, and what the therapist thought would be most beneficial for Monica. We both felt comfortable moving forward with the match so we arranged for me to meet with Monica's adoptive mother. Our meeting also went well and helped us both better understand how the match would work–when I would be able to visit with Monica and for how long, what activities her mom approved of or discouraged, how we would deal with changes in the schedule, etc. Now that I had gone through all the preliminary steps, I was ready to meet Monica.

Our first few visits were a little awkward, as in most cases when one is getting to know somebody new, but after two or three months of regular visits, we had a pretty comfortable rapport. We visited museums, went to the zoo, had lunch, saw movies, hung out at my house, did crafts, listened to music, and talked about all sorts of things. We gradually learned about each other and discovered many common interests. Just like any friendship, ours has ups and downs but we've learned to ride them out together. And, like any friendship, it is the most basic and simple things that we've come to most appreciate about each other.

Monica is not much of a talker when it comes to feelings, but each Christmas for the last three years, she's written me a letter. This Christmas, her words brought me to tears in the middle of a visit to Friendly's: "You really are my best friend in the world. You know those people I call friends, they aren't really my friends because I know they talk about me. But you don't talk about me, or only in a good way . . . I am so happy I have someone I can tell all my secrets to . . . If anybody would be a role model to me it would be you . . . Your son, your husband, and you are my true friends."

The Compeer organization is a wonderful resource in our community because it celebrates and facilitates the power of friendship. I have been the beneficiary of that power and now, as a full time staff member of Compeer, I seek to engage as many people as I can in volunteering to share their friendship with someone in need. I certainly didn't realize how completely this experience would transform my life but I am truly grateful that I made the call to become a Compeer volunteer.

She Cheers Me On!

Cindy Gillen

My Compeer is a very special lady. She's very classy and sophisticated, yet down to earth too. She has style and knows how to dress. She is very pretty, with blonde hair and blue eyes, and has a soft voice. Her name is Yvonne. She has impacted my life in many ways. She always cheers me on. I am schizoaffective, but I have recovered enough that I do speaking engagements around the city for the National Alliance for the Mentally Ill (NAMI). She always supports me and tries to come and hear me. Whenever I finish speaking somewhere she tells me how good I am.

Yvonne also taught me deep-breathing exercises. Sometimes in the morning I have hallucinations and see things on the ceiling of my bedroom. I use her technique until they pass. And it works!

Once when the Iraq war first broke out and they were doing the "shock and awe" over Baghdad, I couldn't take it anymore. I lived with my mom then. Every night she would turn on the 5:00, 6:00, and 6:30 P.M. news. It was all about war. It was upsetting me greatly. It was making my illness act up. But I couldn't tell my mom what was bothering me. Finally I told Yvonne and she had the perfect solution. She took me to Wal-Mart where we got a personal portable CD player with headphones and some CDs. When the news came on, the headphones went on my ears. End of problem! Yvonne saves the day. See how caring she is without upsetting my mom?

My Compeer goes shopping with me to Kohl's, Hobby Lobby, Wal-Mart, Ayres, Walgreens, and other places. We have fun shopping. She also takes me out to lunch and insists on paying. We go to Carlos O'Kelly, Applebee's, and Pizza Hut. We go to the Fort Wayne Art Museum and love it. We look at the paintings and hand-blown glass and quilts and marvel over them. Sometimes if it's nice we take a walk. We are both Christians so we have a lot in common. She's teaching me how to knit this fall so I will have something to do besides writing poetry this winter. She knitted me a scarf last Christmas. I am looking forward to learning how to knit! I have already had one lesson and I did pretty well.

Yvonne travels a lot and always sends me a postcard whenever she goes. She always brings me back a present. She has brought me back a cute purse, money from Canada, a key chain, and other souvenirs.

She is like a mom, a sister, an aunt, and a best friend all rolled into one person and I love her dearly. She's seventy and I'm forty-seven, but we're the same age in spirit. She is a sweet, caring, loving person, and she really cares about me. She's been my Compeer for five years and I would like to make it five more! She's a blessing! God definitely blessed me with her when she came into my life.

Compeer Saved My Life

Carol Cohen

When I heard about Compeer, I had just gotten out of the hospital and was in a respite facility. The Compeer program literally saved my life and has been an invaluable experience. I can only imagine how many other people this program has helped.

My case manager came to me with information about Compeer and asked if I were interested. She explained the program to me and she and I filled out some paper work. With that information Judi Evans, the Compeer coordinator, was able to connect me with a friend who has the same interests as I do as well as similar likes and dislikes. As soon as I met Chris, I was quite pleased and impressed with how well matched we were and what a good job Judi did at placing us together. At first I was a little nervous to meet my Compeer friend but it was done in a safe environment with people I was familiar with. We talked and talked and made plans to meet again the following week. Since then, Chris has been a wonderful friend, confidante and a key part of my life. She has always been there for me and I will always be there for her. Without her help and support I would not have the daily courage to go on. She has given me the strength to cope with my struggle through the bad times. I can finally see the light at the end of the tunnel again. Compeer has helped me to stay out of the hospital and it has also helped me to maintain my stability. There were many times when I was so discouraged that I would have loved to permanently end the pain, forever. I no longer want to curl up and cry. I don't even have the need to isolate. Compeer has made such a positive difference in my life; it is literally my support system and lifeline.

Compeer has played a major role in helping me as well as helping my family. Judi Evans has given us access to important information and resources on how to cope with the responsibilities of every day life. The Compeer program has also helped us to manage and understand my mental illness. We are truly grateful for the wonderful people and their help as well as Compeer's support. Judi has shown genuine care towards me. She has also helped me not to feel so alone in the fight against mental illness. Compeer has also introduced me to many others within my community, some that suffer from mental illness like I do and some who do not. I know that I can trust them all and that they will not judge me for the things I say or do. They understand me. These people, through Compeer, have given me so much emotional support as well as helped me with my daily struggle to cope.

Besides having my Compeer friend there are many activities that are financed through Compeer. I am receiving social security so my budget does not allow me to go out and enjoy myself. Even if I had the finances I would not go out alone as I feel very uncomfortable doing things by myself. Now, when I want to do something, all I have to do is call my Compeer buddy, Chris. Some of the things we enjoy doing together include going to the movies, lunch, walks on the beach and long talks at the local coffee shop. We also have the opportunity to do other things as well, such as museums and the zoo. The most important part of Compeer is knowing I can call Chris anytime and that she will be there for me and will listen to what I have to say. If I have a problem I know I can turn to Chris and I know that she will not judge me. She has been there for me when I have been faced with a crisis situation to talk me through and help me to know there was hope. When I have been in tears she gave me the encouragement and strength to cope. For that I'm very grateful and could never thank her enough or Compeer for placing her in my life.

Compeer also offers programs that help people to live on their own. The programs are fun and informative such as cooking classes. The class taught me healthy eating as well as food preparation and I also got the opportunity to socialize with others who did not have an illness. I also attended a sewing class and worked with a group to create and sew a quilt. The class taught me what teamwork is all about. We made a quilt that will be auctioned off at a charity event and I can't even begin to explain how proud this made me feel.

Someday I hope to be a mentor to a child that has a mental illness. I look forward to being able to help someone else understand their illness. I would let them know that they are not alone and I would reassure them that they don't need to feel lonely and ashamed. But for now, I need to maintain my own stability. Once I am stable then I can think about being a Compeer to someone and giving back all that I have been given.

I often sit and think about how much Compeer has helped me and I smile because I know that there are thousands of other people who feel the same way I do.

An Angel Named Len

George Scott

You never know when and how one person may change your life. "Len" changed mine. We met through the Compeer program in 1987. He was sixty-eight; I was thirty-seven. Ours was like an older brother/younger brother relationship.

Len had his challenges. He was slightly stooped and barrel-chested from emphysema. A pack of cigarettes was always present in his wrinkled shirt pocket. His breathing was troubled. His walk, slow. His sincere smile often present. During our all-too-short twenty-five month friendship (which ended with his passing) Len taught me, directly and indirectly, about compassion, patience, unconditional friendship, humility, dignity, the value of seizing the moment and the healthiness of winning. I also gained understanding about the perils of smoking, the depths of depression, and the mercy of death.

Here is how some of my lessons were learned.

Smoking's effect and patience. Len started smoking at a young age. He often smoked up to two packs of non-filtered Chesterfields each day. Diagnosed with emphysema in the late 1970s, an intense house fire worsened his condition just before Christmas, 1984. Len had fallen asleep on the couch while smoking. His skin and lungs were severely burned. He was not expected to live. After three months in a burn unit he was moved into a supervised facility.

Three years later, when we met, his wheezing had shortened his walking to no more than a dozen steps at a time, between five-minute rest periods.

We always proceeded at a pace comfortable for Len. Our various destinations could wait.

Compassion. Len and his wife Frances were in their late thirties when they married in May 1958. Their love encompassed a special understanding of each other's challenges. Len also had a slight limp from childhood polio and constant problems connected to Apert's Syndrome. Frances had scoliosis. General day-to-day activities quickly exhausted her. When she died in 1976, Len's family members felt he was crushed and never fully recovered from her death, which explains the unspoken sorrow that was always a conversational undercurrent. I learned of his wife from one of Len's sisters only after his passing. Grief management is always personal. Not mentioning Frances was Len's way of handling his.

Dignity. We each liked ice cream cones. Len, vanilla. Me, chocolate. Often, we stopped at one particular ice cream stand. Initially, I paid for the cones. But, one day, Len insisted on paying. I wrongly resisted his efforts. I should have known better. The cost of the cones was small. But the dignity he felt by paying was invaluable. From that point forward, we took turns paying for the cones.

Seizing the moment. Len and I were to spend the morning of Christmas 1987 with his sisters and their families. The rest of the day would be spent playing euchre at my home. However, just moving Len from his hospital room to my car nearly stopped the day before it started. The approvals for Len's holiday activities came with a wheelchair requirement. Uh, oh. I had never before guided anyone in a wheelchair. "How hard could it be?" I thought. Len, wearing his winter coat, took his seat.

He stabilized a medications package in his lap with his left hand, held a spare oxygen tank between his legs, guided a carted oxygen tank in front with his right hand, and attempted to control troublesome plastic tubing while I provided the push and stability. Within a few minutes, we came upon a sharp turn onto a downward slanted hallway. Our unique convoy took the corner wide. My belt-hiding waistline came in handy as I leaned my weight into the turn to keep the wheelchair upright. Fortunately, the office door just around the corner remained closed. We almost glanced off the wall just past the door.

Nothing and no one toppled or crashed. A few feet further, the declining hallway leveled off, just before the outside doors. As we regained our composure, Len looked up at me with the biggest grin I had ever seen on his face. He worked one of his hands free and we "high-fived." We were collectively grateful the few seconds had been only exhilarating and not disastrous.

The healthiness of winning. About two weeks after we met, Len asked me if I played euchre. "That's a card game . . . right?" I responded. With a broad, confident smile he graciously said, "I'll teach you."

He did. Len was a euchre master. "I play to win," he declared one day. "I expect you to play to win, too." "You're on," I said. We enjoyed the head-to-head competition. Neither of us backed down from the other. However, he thoroughly thrashed me almost every time we played.

Playing euchre became a mainstay in our friendship. If the weather kept us indoors, we played many games. If we were headed out, we snuck in a quick game or two. But one thing struck me as we played–Len appeared healthier, especially during the first eighteen months of our friendship. He coughed less. He sat straighter in the chair. His voice was clearer. His movements were smoother and more confident. His healthier demeanor also surfaced when Len capably handled a cue stick as we competitively played pocket billiards. And, yes . . . he thrashed me at that, too.

Depths of depression. In the summer of 1988, Len had been stopped from jumping from a sixth floor window and was receiving treatment at a local hospital. When the news reached me, I hurried to see him. Upon my arrival, I was ushered to the activity room, where nearly all the patients were watching TV. Although seated with the others, Len seemed very much alone. "George is here," the nurse said, touching his forearm.

He slowly raised his head. His appearance jolted me. His dark, sunken eyes were full of fear. They appeared to scream out for help from somewhere deep inside him. I will never forget the image.

Moving to a nearby table, we began to talk. I am not sure what I said. I wasn't quite sure what I should have said. We just talked. The intensity in his eyes gradually lessened.

Len's condition suppressed his appetite. Concerned that he would not receive the proper, and much needed, nourishment, the staff felt coaxing from a friend or family member would help. His two sisters lived and worked over thirty miles from the hospital. My office was only minutes away and my schedule was more flexible. The collective decision was that I would help Len at lunch and dinner. Over the next couple weeks, Len's appetite returned and his mood brightened. His eyes regained their normal appearance.

Humility. Compeer celebrated its 15th anniversary in 1988. Len and I were asked to be the friendship highlighted on a local TV station's evening news *Bright Spot*. "If it's OK with Len, it's OK with me," I answered, uncertain as to how Len would actually feel.

"Yes," he stated with a resolve I had not seen before. "There's something I want to say."

We were videotaped playing pool. Then we were interviewed individually. I mentioned how Len's friendship helped me stay positive throughout some personal life negatives. Then it was Len's turn. He seemed impatient as he answered the first few questions. Then he said what he had wanted to say, "George saved my life, more than once."

I had had no idea. I always enjoyed Len's company. I had hoped he might have enjoyed mine. To this day, I am humbled by his words and honored by our friendship.

Death's mercy. One day, in August 1989, I walked into Len's hospital room, failing to notice the "mask needed" door sign. We settled in to play euchre. A nurse entered the room and pointed to the sign, showing concern. Not wanting to isolate Len in his own hospital room, I waved her off. Strangely, I felt immune to Len's advanced-stage illness.

On my next visit, I *had* to wear both a hospital mask AND latex gloves. Len's eyes showed his hurt. However, he assured me no apologies were needed.

That day, we talked about playing euchre, but never did. We just talked. Melancholy filled the room. Although he never said it, I felt as though Len knew his end was near. Less than a week later, he died. No more emphysema. No more depression. No more residual polio effects. No more suffering. Len was now at peace.

It was too coincidental. Len's passing was just two weeks before my new business venture opened its doors. Much time during the summer had been spent developing and implementing a business plan, with partners. "Good luck, George," I *felt* Len say to me a couple days after his funeral. "You don't need me any more. You'll do fine."

That is when it hit me! Over the past couple years, I had had a couple significant challenges outside our relationship. Len's friendship had carried me through. His work with me *was* done.

Because of all that Len taught me, one way or another, and because of his final words of encouragement, I felt Len was indeed an angel in disguise. I still do.

Through the Eyes of a Child

Jose Fernandez

In my much younger years, I have known loneliness and have witnessed the lives of desolation and fear that many emotionally and mentally ill people experience. As a youngster, barely twelve years of age and newly arrived in this country, I have experienced culture and language shock; these were feelings that were exacerbated when my mother was institutionalized with mental illness and I was left alone with a loving, yet distraught grandmother. How I craved then for some understanding soul to befriend me; someone who having experienced life would gently tell me that this too shall pass, but back then, there was no Compeer. There was no organization that would match a needy youngster with a compassionate friend.

Upon taking early retirement in 1992, I became aware of the significant role that Compeer plays in many people's lives and of the many youth who need the emotional support and caring that compassionate givers could provide. Through the auspices of Compeer, I met two wonderful kids. The first one, "Luis," was around ten years old when we first met. He was a very personable boy blessed with a great sense of humor. He observed that often I carried a magazine with me and asked me why. To this I responded, to utilize my time while I waited for him. The following time we met, he brought a comic book. When I asked him why, he responded with a shy smile, "in case you are too boring."

For him, I was the only male figure in his life on whom he could depend. For me, he represented a fresh look at life, a chance to relive part of my youth. We did many things: discussed homework assignments, ate together, and attended Compeer picnics and Halloween parties. Luis and I maintained our Compeer relationship for six years until growing up interests started to take more of his time.

"Marté" and I were matched when he was eight years old and we now have been together for close to four years. He is a bundle of energy, often exploding into a flashing smile! He does not walk; he runs, skips, hops, and does cart wheels. He is a constant motion machine!

We attend many Compeer events together. Of these, his favorite is the Compeer Christmas party for the youth. For the past several years, it has been held at the Rochester Museum and Science Center. There are a lot of interesting activities at the museum that he enjoys participating in. One of his favorites is "rock climbing," but the highlight of the evening for Marté, following the pizza and soft drinks, is the distribution of Christmas presents. Every kid goes home with at least one carefully selected gift.

When I am in town, we try to meet for a couple of hours per week. I usually pick him up at school where he proudly introduces me to his fellow students as his Compeer friend. His classmates look at me with my white hair and have difficulty believing that friendship exists between people with such age difference. So when occasionally some classmate asks, "Is that your grandpa?" he flashes his Hollywood smile and nods his head in agreement. During our visit, he may play some video games at the mall (one of his favorite activities) or go to the library (one of my favorite activities) before going out to eat. We discuss what each of us has done during the week and, when I can convince him, some schoolwork. When I am gone on one of my trips, I send him postcards, and upon returning, we locate on a map the country or city that I have visited, and we discuss specific things of interest in these places.

Marté is a product of an impoverished environment. Although he has a mother who loves him, there are many other things missing in his life.

Besides poor economic conditions, there has never been a steady male role model in his life. He has never met his father; his grandfather is a distant fading image. It is incredible that someone like him, coming from such a difficult start in his life, could have such a sweet disposition. When I am with him, I forget about my own concerns and focus on the things he enjoys, whether his agility with a video game, the state of a good hamburger or doing his moves while dancing at a festival.

I am too much of a realist to think that our two hours per week will change his life. Although, I trust it will leave pleasant memories and there is always the hope that it will leave significant impressions. However, I know for sure that we both look forward with enthusiasm to getting together, and I know that in many ways, he has changed my life.

Some time ago, Marte' asked me a question that I found very moving, "Will we still be friends when we die?" To which I responded, "We will find a way!" I am sure we will.

Inspiration and Hope

Bonnie Phillips

Ours is a wonderful story of love and hope and mutual growth and understanding. It's a story of two people meeting and sharing their time and their hearts, and thus having their lives equally enriched. I had been teaching high school English for over twenty-five years and so I had many young adults in and out of my life, but I felt that I could make a real difference in someone's life in a more personal way. And so a friend led me to call Compeer. We met when "Kate" was ten years old and in the fifth grade at a special school for emotionally disturbed children. Today she is twenty-three. Her journey has been remarkable, and is largely due to Compeer and this very special, inspiring relationship.

During the past thirteen years she has progressed from that school to a special education class in a public school, to mainstreamed high school classes. She was encouraged to apply to college and attended Morrisville Community College on scholarship, graduating cum laude with an Associate's degree in humanities and as a member of Phi Theta Kappa, the college honor society. She applied to four universities to complete a Bachelor of Arts degree, and was accepted at all of them. That fall she entered the State University of New York, College at Geneseo as a transfer student, again with the assistance of several scholarships and grants. I am so proud to tell you that she graduated last month with a Bachelor of Arts degree in sociology from Geneseo.

Now she stands at a real crossroads, one that I am sure is familiar to other Compeer friends and volunteers. Throughout her life Kate has had the support of many people and organizations, including her Compeer friend, caring school guidance counselors, EOP campus offices, and college advisors and tutors. But now she stands looking out at a world ahead where most of those support systems have vanished, and she is a little bit overwhelmed. It is a daunting prospect for all new graduates who have to face getting a job, health insurance, an apartment, a car: in short, putting a whole new life together on their own. As she has left behind the grade school, high school and college support systems, I am so grateful for our Compeer relationship, which is stronger now than ever.

Kate has recently taken the civil service entrance exam and is hoping to go into some aspect of social work. She recognizes all the support and guidance she has been given over her lifetime, and she wants to work in a field where she can give back some of that encouragement to others to make their lives a little bit better. This has been an incredible thirteen-year journey for both of us. She has worked through tremendous fears, insecurities and loneliness. It is so thrilling now to see her opening herself to the world, to new friends and new experiences—tentatively, gently, like a flower opening to the sunshine.

The biggest surprise for me is how much our friendship has changed *my* life. I went into this relationship thinking about what I might be able to do for her. I never realized how much she would do for me. She has taught me the value of intangible things. She has taught me not to take anything for granted. She has taught me to step back from a pre-occupation with those things which so many of us put at the head of our list and to see—and cherish—the true essence of experiences.

Here is one story I can share, which will show you what I have learned from her:

One Christmas night when she was about twelve, we were driving home after spending Christmas day with my husband's family. It had taken hours to open the mountain of presents under the tree. Kate had made—or together we had shopped for and wrapped—small gifts for everyone who was there for the holiday. But unbelievably, no one had thought to get her a single gift. I was so angry with all of them for their thoughtlessness. On the drive home, Kate was very quiet. Thinking that she too might have been hurt by being left out of the Christmas gift giving and that might explain her silence, I gently asked if she was sleeping there in the back seat. "Oh, no!" she exclaimed. "I've been going over every minute of this day in my mind. It was the *best* Christmas I can *ever* remember!!!!" I was grateful for the darkness, which hid my tears of amazement and joy as I was reminded of the true meaning of Christmas—which this little girl had seen so clearly.

In many ways our Compeer friendship is more important now than ever before. Kate has successfully made the transition from high school to

college. She was able to leave home, leave her mother, and leave her familiar routine and the security of her known world. But she did it, and did it
well, discovering along the way that she is a likeable person with talents she
can use to construct a new life for herself. It's hard for her right now to imagine her future and where she will fit into it. But one time, when she was
about seventeen and we were having one of our weekly "sitting-by-the-lake"
talks, she said to me, "Bonnie, the best thing you have given me is hope and
the belief that my life can be different from the life I have known." She is on
her way, and she and I both owe Compeer our heartfelt thanks.

PART II

Clinical Perspectives

II: Clinical Perspectives

Compeer's association with the mental health profession is one of mutual benefit. We provide an adjunct service to psychotherapy and treatment, while mental health professionals provide advice and support to our volunteers. Clinicians play a vital role in the Compeer team. They initiate the matching process by referring their patients to us. They remain involved throughout the life of a match by monitoring and guiding the success of the relationship. In the following six chapters you will read about Compeer's impact from the perspectives of seven clinicians. These authors represent the viewpoints of their specific disciplines and have chosen to focus on different aspects of Compeer's role as an adjunct to therapy.

In chapter five, Dr. J. Steven Lamberti, a psychiatrist, discusses the value of Compeer as a form of intervention for persons with schizophrenia. In chapter six, Dr. Kathleen Coyne Plum, a nurse, relates her experience as a referring clinician and also describes the Compeer volunteer training program that was created by her graduate nursing students. In chapter seven, Michele Beeley, a clinical social worker, discusses the value of the Compeer program for adolescents and children. In chapter eight, Dr. Stephen Dvorin, a psychiatrist, details the various benefits of Compeer to the patient-client, to the patient-volunteer, and to the mental health professional. In chapter nine, Dr. John S. McIntyre, a psychiatrist, discusses the impact of Compeer on patients, particularly in the areas of isolation, lack of stimulation, monotony, and low self-esteem. In the same chapter, Ann McIntyre, M.A., a professor of psychology, describes the connection between Monroe Community College and Compeer. Finally, in chapter ten, psychologist Richard M. Ryan, explores how several ideas concerning friendship and volunteerism are central to the Compeer mission, both in terms of the way Compeer helps its clients, and its recruitment and training of volunteers.

5. Compeer in the Care of Adults with Schizophrenia

J. Steven Lamberti, M.D.

As the earlier chapters in this book have described, Compeer is a volunteer-based agency founded in 1973 with the mission of providing companions to persons suffering from mental illness. Despite the importance of that mission, there is a tendency among clinicians to minimize the value of volunteer-based services simply because they are voluntary. I was such a clinician when I completed psychiatry residency training at the University of Rochester Medical Center. But my views have since changed. This chapter will share subsequent professional experiences that have lead me to draw two conclusions about the role of Compeer in the care of persons with schizophrenia:

1. Compeer offers vital services that healthcare professionals cannot provide.
2. Compeer volunteers are worth their weight in gold.

A Discovery

Throughout the past twenty years, training programs for psychiatrists, psychologists, nurses, social workers and family therapists have tended to focus on teaching various forms of individual, group, and family interventions. While the importance of volunteer-based services like Compeer may be acknowledged, it is typically not *emphasized* in the training of mental health professionals. As a result, most professionals learn about the role of volunteers through their own work experiences. My first experience with Compeer occurred after residency training, during my neuropsychiatry fellowship. The fellowship consisted of treating patients with schizophrenia by day and dissecting rat brains by night in search of a cure. Although the cure for schizophrenia eluded me, I did make one important discovery. It began with a new patient that I admitted to the hospital. For the purpose of this chapter I will call him Mike.

Mike was a seventeen-year-old Asian immigrant who was hospitalized after becoming psychotic following his entry to the United States. His large and supportive family was alarmed by the symptoms that Mike had developed over a six-month period. Normally friendly and outgoing, Mike had lost interest in his usual activities and had begun secluding himself in his bedroom. He had also begun staying up late and wandering the house at night. During the months prior to admission, Mike's thinking had become increasingly disorganized to the point that family members had difficulty understanding him. In addition, he had grown increasingly preoccupied with thoughts that their home was filled with "devils." Mike did not eat or sleep during the week prior to hospitalization. He was subsequently taken to the hospital by ambulance after smashing the family's television because it was "spying."

In the hospital Mike willingly accepted antipsychotic medication and was often visited by his family as they struggled to understand what was happening to him. Mike's eating and sleeping began to improve within days of beginning the medication. His English was very poor but he managed to communicate using simple phrases. He also liked to draw. The hospital had an art therapist and Mike participated actively in art therapy sessions. His initial drawings were no more than disorganized scribbles. As his psychosis resolved, his drawings began to depict him doing various activities with family members. The day before leaving the hospital, Mike drew a picture of himself standing in a room with people of different colors. The drawing was entitled "Friends."

I began seeing Mike and his family members together in our outpatient clinic following his discharge. Each time we met I asked them the same questions. "How's it going? Any problems with the medication?" The replies were always the same. "It's going okay. The medicine is okay." But Mike didn't look happy. He always wore the same clothes and he seldom spoke or smiled. He did not seem to fit in at the local high school. During one of our sessions his mother explained to me, "this is a different country."

A few weeks later, I discussed Mike's case with a social work colleague in order to secure his health insurance. I mentioned in passing that his antipsychotic medication was working but that he may need an antidepressant. She replied, "You should give him Compeer." *"Compeer?"* I exclaimed, never having heard of that medication. Sensing my confusion, she gave me a Compeer brochure and said, "Check them out; they're worth their weight in gold."

I had a hard time explaining Compeer to Mike and his family. Luckily I had their trust and a copy of the brochure in my pocket. With their permission I completed the necessary paperwork and submitted an application on Mike's behalf. A month later an undergraduate college student called my office to make an appointment. My secretary told him that I wasn't accepting any new patients. Undaunted, he explained to her that he wasn't a patient; he was a Compeer volunteer. My secretary made an appointment for him to meet with me the following week.

Rich was an undergraduate liberal arts major who wanted to give something back to his community. He was pleasant and likeable but I didn't know if he was right for Mike. Rich was a fraternity member, clean cut and well dressed. He and Mike came from different worlds. After getting acquainted with Rich, I explained Mike's situation to him. I told him about Mike's mental illness and encouraged him to call as needed. I also advised him to avoid exposing Mike to loud or overly stimulating environments.

Mike was smiling the next time I saw him in my office. He brought with him a drawing depicting a raucous scene in a crowded ice arena. It was entitled "Hockey Game." Mike told me how Rich had taken him to his first hockey game, and how much he enjoyed cheering along with all of Rich's fraternity brothers. His mother said with a wink and nod "I think they adopt him." *Adopt* him! At that moment I realized what Mike had been lacking: A peer group, a role model, a sense of belonging. An opportunity to acculturate. It struck me that these missing ingredients were now available, thanks to a volunteer.

Mike made several noticeable changes over the course of the following year. The first thing to go was his clothing. Thanks to some hand-me-downs from Rich and the fraternity brothers, Mike adopted a snappy collegiate look. He began carrying himself with more confidence. Mike's grades at school improved significantly. He became interested in attending college. His language improved too, incorporating a variety of colorful new expressions such as "My mom's too *uptight*. Our goalie *kicks ass*. Math is a *total drag*." And my favorite of all: "Doc, you're *awesome!*"

I lost track of Mike when I completed the fellowship. He was entering college at the time and was showing every indication of success. Considering Mike's improvement in retrospect, it is clear that many factors contributed to it. He had a supportive family, and he received effective pharmacotherapy. On the other hand, Mike's family had always been there for him and good medications were readily available. Looking back on Mike's progress, I believe that the turning point came when I referred him to Compeer. Compeer provided a valuable human resource, something that neither his family nor his doctor could provide. A rare and precious element, as good as gold.

A Clinical Perspective

Mike's vignette illustrates how Compeer volunteers can have a positive and lasting impact upon the lives of individuals with severe mental illnesses. "Severe mental illness" is a term that represents a broad group of psychiatric disorders characterized by the presence of potentially disabling symptoms such as hallucinations and delusions. This section will present schizophrenia as a primary example of serious mental illness, and will discuss the special role of Compeer in the care of adults with this disorder.

Overview of Schizophrenia

Schizophrenia is arguably the most severe and disabling of all mental illnesses. Far from rare, schizophrenia affects 1% of all individuals. In the United States, that number is equivalent to the combined metropolitan populations of Boston, Miami and Las Vegas. Schizophrenia is a brain disease, not something that is caused by poor parenting or created by society. It is a serious condition that leads one in ten individuals who suffer from it to end their lives by suicide. Another 10% will recover completely with no further signs or symptoms after an initial episode. For the majority of persons with schizophrenia, however, it is a relapsing and unrelenting illness that poses lifelong challenges.

Schizophrenia is difficult to diagnose because there are no imaging techniques, blood tests, or laboratory measures to assist in the diagnostic process. Diagnosis is based on the presence and course of clinically observable signs and symptoms over time. Current diagnostic criteria for schizophrenia require the presence of signs and symptoms of the illness for at least six months before the diagnosis can be made.[1] This lengthy diagnostic process can be frustrating for persons with the illness as well as their family members and friends.

Symptoms of schizophrenia can be broadly divided into two groups: positive symptoms and negative symptoms. Positive symptoms include hallucinations, delusions, and disorganized behavior. While these can be frightening and bewildering for those who experience them as well as those who witness them, positive symptoms generally respond well to antipsychotic medications. Negative symptoms consist of loss of motivation, energy, and the ability to enjoy things. Although they are less striking than positive symptoms, negative symptoms are more disabling. Unfortunately, negative symptoms tend not to respond well to any existing medications.

Recovery and the Role of Compeer

The value of Compeer as an intervention for persons with schizophrenia can be readily understood in the context of recovery. The term "recovery" has long been used in treatment of persons with chemical dependency but has only recently emerged with respect to mental illness. In his seminal paper

"Recovery from Mental Illness: The Guiding Vision of the Mental Health Service System in the 1990s" Anthony defines recovery as a process whereby persons with mental illness can learn to live satisfying, hopeful, and contributing lives.[2] Rather than implying a cure, recovery means developing a new meaning and purpose in life despite the presence of mental illness. Anthony notes that the recovery process is a deeply personal and unique process of changing one's values, skills, and/or roles. While no two individuals take precisely the same path, certain factors are likely to facilitate the recovery process. As a psychiatrist, my initial impulse is to think that psychiatric treatment, including medications and various forms of counseling, is the most important factor. However, those who have been through the process often cite the support of friends and family members as being equally if not more important.

Schizophrenia poses a formidable barrier to recovery because it separates people from their natural supports. The disease typically becomes apparent during the early to mid twenties, a time when most individuals are forming new friendships through school, jobs, or other activities. People with schizophrenia often experience a marked loss of energy, motivation, and ability to enjoy their usual activities. These negative symptoms can also make it difficult to maintain or initiate friendships. Schizophrenia can have a particularly devastating impact if it begins during the formative teenage years, a time when social skills are developing. Individuals diagnosed with schizophrenia may lack both the necessary skills and the drive to build meaningful relationships. Schizophrenia also poses difficult challenges for families. It is common for parents to narrow their circle of friends as they become increasingly involved in caring for a loved one with schizophrenia. In situations where schizophrenia and drug addiction occur together, the patient and family members can become alienated from one another because of behaviors that have become intolerable.

An additional barrier to recovery is the issue of stigma. People with schizophrenia are often misunderstood as being dangerous, possessed, or lazy. Such images are commonly portrayed in magazines, on television, and on the radio. These misconceptions can have a very negative impact on the self-esteem of those struggling to cope with schizophrenia, and can cause acquaintances to avoid them in social situations. As a result of these multiple factors, many people who suffer from schizophrenia become socially isolated.

Under the best circumstances, those who enter treatment will have access to a variety of services. In addition to medications and primary medical care, these include individual and group therapy, family psychoeducation, case management, day treatment programs, vocational rehabilitation, and residential services. While these services may be necessary in promoting recovery, they are not sufficient for many individuals. I can recall one particular patient who attended a day treatment program and lived in a group home. He seemed to have many friends at each place. One day he asked me to refer him to Compeer. When I asked him why, he replied, "Because I want at least one friend who's not a patient or a therapist."

For some individuals with schizophrenia, a Compeer volunteer is the only person outside of the mental health system with whom they have regular contact. Compeer can have a normalizing influence on such individuals, engaging them in mainstream activities that are interesting and enjoyable. While many of us take for granted attending movies, spectator sports, or music events, most would agree that recreational activities are important to our own mental health. Such activities are often in short supply for people with schizophrenia due the combined impact of negative symptoms and social stigma. In the absence of healthy alternatives, many persons with schizophrenia succumb to the use of illicit drugs and alcohol. Compeer volunteers play a key role in helping to overcome barriers by providing social and recreational opportunities. In addition to opportunities, Compeer volunteers can provide the support and encouragement necessary to spark the involvement of persons with schizophrenia.

Compeer also provides a chance for people coping with schizophrenia to engage in meaningful social relationships. Compeer volunteers and clients often develop a strong mutual sense of trust, enjoyment, and appreciation. While the same can be said of relationships between persons with schizophrenia and mental health professionals, an important distinction exists. The mental health professional's goal is to serve the patient, a goal that involves putting the patient's best interests first at all times. By contrast, the goal of the Compeer volunteer is to develop a meaningful friendship. This goal involves equality, sharing, and a "realness" often lacking in the relationships of persons with schizophrenia. The equality and sharing provided by Compeer are necessary ingredients in the recovery process for many persons with schizophrenia. Describing her relationship with a Compeer volunteer, a patient of mine recently remarked, "She's like the sister I never had."

Conclusion

Since my initial experiences with Mike I have referred more than one hundred patients to Compeer. With few exceptions, the experiences of my patients have been very positive. It is important to recognize that the success of Compeer relationships depends upon the presence of compatibility or "chemistry" between the volunteer and client. Those relationships that become the most enduring typically begin as volunteer-client relationships and gradually become genuine friendships. The therapeutic power of friendship should not be underestimated. Compeer volunteers provide social opportunity as well as a motivational spark that are vital to the recovery of persons with schizophrenia. Compeer can't replace mental health professionals, but it can contribute substantially to mental health outcomes.

Since beginning in Rochester in 1973, Compeer has been recognized by the National Institute of Mental Health as an innovative program for persons with mental illness. Today Compeer is a model mental health organization with more than one hundred affiliates in the United States, Canada, and Australia. My experiences with Compeer have led me to incorporate it into my teaching of medical students, residents, and other mental health professionals. A Compeer referral should be considered for any patient who is socially isolated and lacking in supports. For such individuals, Compeer can be a turning point on the road to recovery.

Notes

1. *Diagnostic and Statistical Manual of Mental Disorders.* (2000) Fourth Edition, Text. Revised (DSM-IV). American Psychiatric Association, Washington, D.C.

2. Anthony, W. A. (1993) Recovery from mental illness: The guiding vision of the mental health service system in the 1990s. *Psychosocial Rehabilitation Journal,* 16(4) 11–23.

6. A Nursing Perspective

Kathleen Coyne Plum, Ph.D., R.N., N.P.P.

The worst solitude is to be destitute of sincere friendship.

–Sir Francis Bacon

All too often, our most vulnerable citizens face isolation, solitude, and lone-liness on a daily basis. Many studies have documented that those having a severe mental illness have social networks that are smaller and denser than those of the general population (Hammer, 1963; Lipton et al., 1981; Holmes-Eber & Riger, 1990). And, without the initiative and skills to reestablish crucial links, the ability of persons with severe mental illness to achieve and maintain recovery is substantially compromised. The Compeer program recognized early on, however, that everyone needs a friend to share frustrations and accomplishments, tears and laughter, in order to have a genuine sense of mental and physical well-being.

Research has also documented the role of social networks as a conduit for social support, and the professional literature abounds with studies that demonstrate that the quality and quantity of social relationships are crucial to health and well-being (Kaplan et al. 1977; Schaefer et al., 1981; Pilusik & Parks, 1986). Nursing theory also views the social domain of the person as key to achieving and maintaining health (King, 1971; Neuman, 1982). Thus, from the beginning, Nursing and Compeer have been naturally compatible organizations, sharing a philosophy that has embraced a strength-based and person-centered approach to health and mental health. I was particularly fortunate to experience Compeer from all aspects of the Nursing Unification Model–practice, education, and research–during my sixteen years as an advanced practice nurse at the University of Rochester Medical Center.

The First Referral

As a therapist in the Adult Ambulatory Clinic at Strong Memorial Hospital, I was acutely aware of the social isolation that many of my clients experienced on a daily basis. Back in the mid-1970s, many of my clients were being discharged to the community after having spent extended stays in the state psychiatric facility. While in the hospital, connections to family, friends, and community were often severely disrupted. Although treatment helped promote and sustain recovery, re-establishment of social connections required more tangible assistance. The then "Adopt-A-Patient" program provided socialization for people still in the hospital. Under the new direction of Bernice Skirboll, however, the program realized that friendship relationships needed to reach out beyond the walls of the institution and out into the community, where individuals were now living. Even with the growing movement toward deinstitutionalization and shorter stays in psychiatric facilities, social isolation and lack of support continued to burden individuals having a chronic and severe mental illness. But by changing the name to Compeer in 1977, the program was able to project a stronger sense of recovery and empowerment, and to move away from the more dependent connotation of "adoption." Mutual support became the cornerstone of success, as volunteers and their matches give and take in a relationship based upon equality.

My first experience with a Compeer referral occurred around 1978–79. The referral process involved a meeting with the volunteer, and this meeting was very reassuring to me. Even though I knew volunteers were screened, it still was good to meet the person who was volunteering, to see if they had the right disposition for this individual (and vise versa), and to give the volunteer suggestions about ways to establish a rapport. My first match was a success, and nothing breeds success like success! As a result, I came to consider Compeer as a potential referral for any client who reported dissatisfaction with his or her social network, had a desire for more socialization, and was unlikely to be able to initiate social relationships on his or her own. It was another important vehicle to promote recovery. I witnessed several clients blossom in confidence as a result of the relationship with their volunteer, engage in activities that previously would have been too anxiety-provoking, and then move into group socialization with their volunteer at Compeer functions, something that would have been unthinkable only months before.

Student Placements

Several years later, in the early and mid-1980s, I added graduate teaching to my responsibilities within the Unification Model. One of the benefits of this was that I coordinated a graduate nursing course entitled Mental Health Promotion and Mental Illness Prevention. Finding student clinical placements that were *not* treatment-oriented was often a challenge. Compeer provided an excellent opportunity for students to work with an organization that was devoted to health promotion, as friendships are clearly important to maintaining one's health, both physical and emotional.

Several students chose the Compeer clinical experience, and took on the roles of teacher and coach. Students developed curricula for volunteers, including information about mental illness and its effect on individuals, families, and friends; current treatments for mental illnesses, including medications, both therapeutic and adverse effects; and, skills in helping others, such as active listening and problem-solving. Students also provided ongoing support to volunteers, giving suggestions regarding ways to promote trust among those who were fearful or ways to avoid unproductive conflicts over issues that were unsolvable. They facilitated socialization in the larger group activities sponsored by Compeer for volunteers and their friends, which made use of other skills by volunteers and peers alike. And a new variation–assisting those in recovery to become volunteers to others working toward recovery–afforded clients the opportunity to use their recovery to help others. Compeer was one of the first programs to promote peer advocacy, and to recognize the value of peer-to-peer relationships. Students were quick to see the health promotion benefits of this model for both the volunteer and the person matched.

Research and Policy Implications

When I took the plunge and undertook nursing doctoral studies at the University of Rochester, my interest in the heath benefits of social relationships led me to select the concept of social network as the centerpiece of my dissertation research. I became interested in the natural network of family, friends and/or co-workers of individuals with chronic, severe mental illness, as well as those social connections that evolved from the rehabilitation system–including Compeers, therapists, case managers, social club members, and/or fellow workshop employees. Using a longitudinal data set, I was able to look at the composition of natural and "constructed" networks, and the degree of interface between these two types of networks (Plum, 1993). While only 2% of the individuals in my sample were known to have a Compeer volunteer, the interaction between the treatment provider and Compeer volunteers was quite high, reflecting the supportive value of relationships that are interconnected. And, in fact, the research substantiated that the intimacy and frequency of social relationships, such as between Compeers and their matches, were significantly related to lower scores on measures of disability for this population.

This research only served to highlight for me the importance of social networks in relation to recovery from mental illness, and the public policy implications inherent in funding programs that create and maintain a system of social network support for those with chronic and severe mental illness.

Compeer Today and Tomorrow

Throughout the course of my career, I have had the opportunity to see how Compeer has made a difference in the lives of individuals recovering from mental illness from several different vantage points. I have also been able to witness the growth of the fledgling "Adopt-A-Patient" program into the internationally renowned program that Compeer is today. Compeer chapters across the nation have developed unique and innovative programs to meet local needs. Some chapters in New York have worked with schools of nursing to help to students understand the nature of mental illness and the importance of a recovery orientation, through a relationship with a peer volunteer. The American Psychiatric Nurses Association's New York Chapter is providing volunteers to develop a training curriculum for Compeer volunteers on co-occurring mental illness and chemical addiction.

Creative ideas for partnerships with other organizations are always welcomed by Compeer. For example, the organization is currently designing new services to support adults in achieving independence and recovery from mental illness through the Western New York Care Coordination Project. The further development of services for children having or at-risk for developing emotional disorders is another goal dear to my heart as county mental health director. Compeer is involved with recreational mentoring for children, and is a member of the mental health team that increasingly includes pediatric/psychiatric nurse practitioners. Compeer has been–and I am confident will continue to be–a partner with nurses and others in responding to the mental health needs of the community well beyond the twenty-first century!

References

Hammer, M. (1963). Influence of small networks as factors in mental hospital readmission. *Human Organization,* 22, 243–51.

Homes-Eber, P. & Riger, S. (1990). Hospitalization and the composition of mental patient's social networks. *Schizophrenia Bulletin,* 16, 157–64.

Kaplan, B. H., Cassel, J. C. & Gore, S. (1977). Social support and health. *Medical Care,* 15 (5), 47–58.

King, I. (1971). *Toward a theory of nursing.* New York: Wiley.

Lipton, F. R., Cohen, C. I., Fischer, E. & Katz, S. E. (1981). Schizophrenia: A network crisis. *Schizophrenia Bulletin,* 7, 144–51.

Neumann, B. (1982). The Neuman systems model: Application to nursing education and practice. Norwalk: Appleton-Century-Crofts.

Pilusik, M. & Parks, S. H. (1986). The healing web: Social networks and human survival. Hanover, NH: University Press of New England.

Plum, K. C. (1993). A longitudinal study of the natural and constructed social networks of chronically mentally ill outpatients in relation to treatment retention, rehospitalization, and measures of psychiatric rehabilitation. Unpublished doctoral dissertation, University of Rochester.

Schaefer, C., Coyne, J. & Lazarus, R. S. (1981). The health-related functions of social support. *Behavioral Medicine,* 4, 381–405.

7. A Social Worker's Perspective on Children and Compeer

Michele Beeley, C.S.W.

I know Compeer as a wonderful program that provides many benefits to people of all ages. Those of us who work in the child mental health area, where treatment options too often are limited, see this additional support as vital. Participation in Compeer includes the benefits of modeling healthy relationships, improved self-esteem, positive use of leisure time, opportunities to utilize new skills learned in therapy, healthy ways to get one-on-one attention, and the broadening of horizons.

Challenges

For outpatient mental health treatment providers, contact with patients is limited by time and location. Perhaps we see someone once every week (or two or three), and oftentimes it is in a clinical setting that is not reflective of the patient's home or community. Partly because of this, the treatment recommendations that we make do not get followed as often as they should. Skills do not get carried over into the "real world." Without this carry-over, progress is severely limited. Compeer provides a conduit into the patient's "real world." For example, Compeer volunteers help patients use social or communication skills that are taught in the office, or to be more active in their free time.

Therapists additionally find that some of the "testing" that patients do is in the form of questioning the mental health professional's motivations: "you just do this for the money" or "you just like to hear about other people's personal business" are statements many clinicians have heard at one time or another. With the Compeer match, questions about motivation are removed from the equation. The volunteer–client relationship seems purer and certainly of a different nature than the therapist–client one.

In the field of child mental health in which I practice, Compeer is especially helpful. We often (though certainly not always) see children who come from homes that are chaotic or dysfunctional. Perhaps the parents have mental health or substance abuse issues of their own. Child abuse or domestic violence can be common in this population. These children may not have a model for "normal" or healthy relationships, nor for patterns of positive interaction with others. Without these models children have difficulty developing healthy relationships of their own. Fortunately, Compeer provides an opportunity for a child to see how a healthy relationship works– one based on kindness and caring, mutuality and respect, without exploitation or expectation.

Practitioners treat many overwhelmed families. The parents may be so frustrated that they ignore their child, or interact in an angry, inappropriate manner. Some of these families have numerous children with multiple needs, limiting the amount of one-to-one time that the patient may get. As a result, some children act out to get the attention that they crave. This can lead to feeling left out at school, being ostracized by peers because they are "different." They may be placed into special classrooms or schools, or even on home tutoring, further isolating them. Compeer helps to decrease isolation and allow for the positive one-on-one attention that is so important to a child's self-esteem, allowing them to know that they as individuals do matter and are worth spending time on. The Compeer friend does not judge, and the fact that the Compeer friend is there by choice, not obligation, adds significantly to the child's sense of being a worthwhile person.

A Compeer Experience

A teenager with whom I worked, who had a Compeer match, said that participating in activities with her Compeer friend gave her the opportunity to get out of her house, allowing her to relax and not worry about the problems at home. According to the patient, learning from these activities that she was actually capable of relaxing gave her the motivation to try some of the recommended relaxation techniques I had given to her. In essence, this led her to be more compliant with treatment recommendations and to make positive progress toward her treatment objectives.

Healthy Modeling

The Compeer friend can also offer a chance for children to learn healthy ways to use leisure time. Many children in treatment come from less than safe neighborhoods, which when coupled with a lack of finances or a depressed or substance abusing parent, means these children have little opportunity to enjoy healthy or wholesome recreation. Children may be kept inside the house, with their only recreation coming in the form of videogames, movies, and television. Compeer friends can take children out of their neighborhoods: to parks where they can get some exercise, to museums, or maybe just for a short respite from a loud and crowded home or neighborhood to a quiet and peaceful library. Finding practical, healthy ways to use leisure time is a common treatment goal and is crucial to making progress with many diagnoses including depression and anxiety disorders.

Opening up children's eyes to educational and career opportunities can also be achieved through Compeer. One child had a volunteer match who was a college student. She would take him to visit the campus and he was in awe of what he saw. This child developed a personal goal of going to college himself. Prior to this experience college was never something he considered seriously, as it wasn't the norm for his family. Many children have only limited awareness of career opportunities, particularly if they live in an economically depressed area. Getting outside of the boundaries of their communities can provide broader horizons for some children. A Compeer friend can also help instill some expectation or belief that a patient is capable of educational and vocational achievement. Just hearing "you can do this, I know you can" empowers a person to set his or her individual goals higher.

Conclusion

Adult mental health programming covers a wide continuum. A variety of social clubs and psychiatric rehabilitation programs in the Rochester community are wonderful assets and a crucial part of mental health treatment. These opportunities, however, do not exist for children and adolescents to the extent that they exist for adult patients. Further, many of the children we see have limited access to typical community and school based extracurricular activities, either because they attend special schools or because their access has been blocked due to behavior problems. For these reasons, Compeer is vitally important and beneficial to children and adolescents.

1. Bernice Skirboll interviews a prospective volunteer, 1976.

2. Congressman Barber Conable presents a Congressional Recognition Award to Bernice Skirboll who accepts it on behalf of Compeer, 1980.

3. Recruitment campaign is unveiled in 1980: "One hour a week can save someone's life."

4. A "Distinguished Volunteer Award," signed by President Ronald Reagan, is awarded in 1982. New York State Senator Alfonse D'Amato, Monroe County Executive Lucien Morin, Bernice Skirboll, and Rochester Mayor Tom Ryan are pictured. (Credit: Ira Srole, photographer, Bureau of Public Information, City of Rochester.)

5. Compeer incorporates in 1983. Alice Raymond, Marcia Hargrove, and Bernice Skirboll pictured.

6. New York State Governor and Mrs. Mario Cuomo present Compeer with the
New York State Eleanor Roosevelt Community Service Award in 1984.

To Bernice,
Best Wishes

7. Bob Dole becomes the Compeer National Spokesperson, 1987.

8. Donna Alvarado (former director of ACTION), Michigan State Governor George Romney, President George H. W. Bush, and M. Norton Rosner (former Compeer Board Chairman), 1989.

9. Andrew Meloni, Jr., Andrew Meloni (retired Monroe County Sheriff), Bernice Skirboll, and Arunas Chesonis at the first annual Compeer Golf Tournament, 1995.

10. Photograph that appeared in *Family Circle* magazine in 1991 accompanying the article, "Women Who Made a Difference."

11. First Lady Rosalynn Carter with Bernice Skirboll at the 1999 Compeer International Conference in Atlanta, Georgia.

12. Tipper Gore with Bernice Skirboll at the first White House Conference on Mental Health, 1999.

13. New York State Congresswoman Louise Slaughter, longtime supporter of Compeer, with Bernice Skirboll.

14. Brenda Levison and Barbara Posson at a Compeer activity.

15. Jose Fernandez and his young Compeer friend enjoy a meal together. Photograph courtesy of the Greece *Messenger Post.* Used by permission. Carrie Ann Grippo staff photographer.

16. Barbara Absi and Brittany Souza, 17, of Coventry, Rhode Island. An article about them appeared in the *Providence Journal* on April 21, 2005. Used by permission of the Providence Journal Company.

17. Andrew driving the Compeer-sponsored entry in the Soap Box Derby.

18. Debra Bonsignore and her Compeer friend.

19. Workshop at the 2004 Compeer International Conference in Wichita, Kansas.

20. Richard Ward, Amy Humphrey (director of Compeer, Binghamton, NY), and Walter Halm during presentation of an award for outstanding Adult Match at the 2004 Compeer International Conference. A Compeer quilt is in the background.

21. Bill Nelson and Hugh Fleischer. Anchorage, Alaska.

22. John Neylan, Carmell Logg, and Margaret Hunskes of Compeer Australia.

23. Phil Pecora and his Compeer friend, fishing along the Erie Canal, Fairport, New York.

24. Mary DeSino and Helena Krebs enjoying bingo.

25. Compeer Executive Committee, October 2005. First row (left to right): Bernice Skirboll, Ben Giambrone, Kathleen Pringle; second row: Phil Fain, Maureen Creary, Tim Cook, and J. Theodore Smith.

26. The staff members of Compeer, Inc. and Compeer International in the organization's offices, October 2005.

8. Compeer: A Psychiatrist's Perspective

Stephen Dvorin, M.D.

I am a psychiatrist: a clinician, an educator, an administrator, and a researcher. For thirty-five years, in both the private and public sectors, I have provided services to individuals with psychiatric disorders. In recent years I have been the medical director of a large (1,100 patients) outpatient psychosocial rehabilitation program for patients[1] with severe and persistent mental illness. My patients have needs, feelings, hopes, and goals that are no different than those of anyone else. And yet, as a physician I know that the lives of those with mental disorders are inherently different from all other "ill" persons. In spite of national movement towards parity, public education, patient rights, peer counseling, and efforts to reduce stigma and discrimination, my patients remain "different." Stigma, feelings of shame or disgrace that patients personally experience, and discrimination, the differential and prejudicial treatment that is imposed by others, have diminished over time but persist in a way that fosters "separateness" from the community. Impairments in family, social, and vocational functioning leave patients under-skilled and isolated. Symptoms of various types lead to avoidance of and by others, whether fearful/paranoid, anxious/avoidant, or shunned because of social skill deficits or odd behaviors. While each individual may vary in the mix of symptoms, impairments, and their consequences, the final common denominator is some degree of isolation. Often family members will provide the support system that facilitates socialization, independent living, and enriched quality of life. However, families of mentally ill persons also experience stigma and discrimination. Receiving less understanding and support than the families of individuals with physical illnesses, they are often isolated and burdened by the demands on them. Therefore, we cannot automatically assume that families can add additional tasks to their full plate of responsibilities. Most patients in traditional mental health treatment lack the community-based resources to enhance social and independent living skills. Even those involved in psychosocial rehabilitation programs may lack the unique community supports that patients need to survive and thrive. What is most often missing is a neutral, comforting, accepting, helpful relationship. Typically a friendship embraces these characteristics. A friend certainly adds some of what is missing in the patient's life and not otherwise available from other resources. Thus, I see the unique niche that Compeer fills. It is not formal treatment; it is not a self-help group; it is not a psychosocial club. It is an extension of the formal treatment team and offers support, companionship, and skills training in a relationship with someone other than a professional mental health provider or family member. Indeed, the Compeer program helps my patient in ways that the formal network of services cannot.

In the late 1970s I was shifting from community psychiatry to private practice. At a time when psychosocial rehabilitation was in its infancy, I sought Compeer volunteers for my patients, and I encouraged more competent, higher functioning patients to serve as volunteers. Over time, I have observed and categorized the benefits that accrue to the treating mental health professional and to the patients who receive and provide Compeer service. In fact, the duality of a provider-patient relationship became the triaxial relationship of provider-Compeer-patient: a new partner was included.

Patient Benefits

The benefits to a patient who is matched with a Compeer include:

1. *Companionship:* The isolated patient has added a new participant in his or her life. There is someone to call on the phone, someone to visit, and someone with whom to socialize in the community. Loneliness is diminished. This is an opportunity for friendship with a neutral, accepting person who has not previously been part of the patient's life. In particular, the new friend is not a member of the patient's family. Old conflict with family members is therefore not played out in this new, potentially more satisfying relationship in which the Compeer volunteer accepts the patient as he or she is, including the presence of symptoms and impairments. What most often follows is a real relationship in which the patient experiences acceptance and fellowship.

2. *Enhanced self-worth:* The life trajectory of those with mental disorders is adversely affected by the symptoms and impairments of the disorder. Symptoms, stigma, discrimination, and failed accomplishments tend to lower self-esteem and self-worth. Many adults with mental disorders were teased or shunned as children and adolescents. Traumatic early life events sometimes lead to shame and embarrassment. Collectively, the result is lowered self-esteem and self-worth.

A Compeer volunteer engenders acceptance, empathy, nurturance, companionship, all of which foster improved self-worth and self-esteem Compeer volunteers promote improved self-image. As Compeer relationships evolve and solidify, patients feel better about themselves. A recent Compeer survey[2] reported 82% of patients experienced improvement in self-esteem since being matched with a Compeer volunteer.

Case Example

A middle-aged man, a college graduate with a bipolar disorder, had long been underemployed. He stated, "I was in a shell, shy and introverted and lacking in confidence." In a multi-year match with a Compeer, also a recipient of psychiatric services and a successful academician, the individual was gently engaged in discussions of movies, art, politics, current events, and other topics. He was encouraged to speak of his experiences at support groups. "He pushed me to do more," the patient noted, and indeed he gradually did so. He explained, "I began to express myself. . . . I started to write stories about my experience. As I was speaking, writing, and expressing myself, my whole outlook changed." And now, he experiences increased self-confidence and self-esteem, directly attributed to his Compeer connection.

3. *Meaningful activity:* Patients, by virtue of symptoms–depressive, psychotic, negative symptoms, cognitive impairments, and anxiety, among others–are often quite limited in their activities. They may lack the capacity to organize and accomplish an activity; they may be uncomfortable enough with people that they will avoid most social contact; or they may lack transportation or financial resources to participate in meaningful activity. Compeer volunteers often have the resources and the wherewithal to suggest, plan, and implement activities. Even a social visit, dinner, or shopping trip may provide more organized and satisfying activity than is otherwise available to patients. Beyond that, the resources of the Compeer program may provide low-cost tickets to a variety of local amusements, or Compeer staff will host theme events such as Valentine's Day, Halloween, or other holiday parties. The Compeer volunteer and the Compeer organizational resources therefore provide abundant opportunities for community-based activities.

4. *Socialization skills:* Social skills can be underdeveloped, or existing social skills may have eroded as a result of mental illness and its accompanying impairments. The Compeer volunteer offers opportunities in every contact with a patient to improve social skills. A

simple social visit allows for traditional greetings and neutral "small talk." Compeers can model social behavior and provide opportunities to rehearse and practice social behaviors. Beyond that, the various activities of eating out, shopping, community events, and Compeer theme parties all provide opportunities for a wide variety of social behaviors to be modeled, learned, and practiced in a benign, supportive, non-judgmental environment.

Case Example

A thirty-five-year-old man with schizophrenia has had many lengthy hospitalizations at a local state hospital and now lives in supervised housing. Persistent psychotic symptoms dating to adolescence have left marked impairments in the domains of social, vocational, and independent living skills. He is generally pleasant, non-violent, but quite helpless and dependent. Even though his family remains involved in his life, he tends delusionally to misinterpret some of their efforts on his behalf. Matched with a Compeer volunteer for the past ten years, he has come to rely on the volunteer for regular contact and companionship, a bit of financial assistance, and reality testing (sometimes with daily phone contact). In a non-judgmental, supportive relationship with a Compeer volunteer, his self-confidence and self-worth have increased. The volunteer has advocated for the patient both in his treatment and housing arrangements. Slowly, the patient has learned more effective social skills in restaurants and convenience stores even as his psychotic symptoms and odd behaviors persist. Reassured by the continuity of the relationship, he has come to rely on the Compeer volunteer for regular, meaningful activities.

5. *Special benefits:* Compeer volunteers can perform special tasks, favors, and services that fall outside the boundaries and constraints of traditional treatment relationships. These are uncommon but meaningful events for patients. Volunteers might assist with transportation for a non-treatment activity such as a ride to a bus or train station. Volunteers with special interests or talents, such as music or computers, often expose their matches to new experiences and hobbies that would otherwise remain foreign to them. Compeer volunteers have advocated for patients for benefits and services. Compeer volunteers often will include patients in their own family activities and celebrations. Although the Compeer organization stages social events and provides reduced-cost admission to community events, the volunteers invariably subsidize their matches when circumstances require. The list of special, unique contributions to patients is endless.

The Benefits to a Patient Who Becomes a Compeer

In discussing this topic, we should note the growing utilization of "peers" (those patients in the mental health system who have been trained to provide services to other patients) to expand the repertoire of services available to patients. Peers have assisted with skills training, advocacy, empowerment, and support activities. New York State has formally recognized the value of trained "peer specialists," and its Medicaid program will pay for certain services that peers provide. Patients who become Compeer volunteers are peers and gain the following benefits:

1. *Improved self esteem:* Given the variably experienced assaults on self-esteem and self-worth noted above, patients inherently feel better about themselves when they are enhancing the well-being of another human being. Volunteering is satisfying and is perceived internally and externally as "the right thing to do." Religious or moral imperatives fuel and support good deeds and helping others. Success and accomplishment are reinforced by positive feedback from matches and from a society that encourages volunteerism. Also, the Compeer organization conducts award celebrations at which volunteers are recognized and honored. Consequently, self-esteem and self-worth are enhanced.

2. *"Giving back"*: The "recipient" or "consumer" of services, by definition, "receives" something or "consumes" or "acquires" services. By the social custom of reciprocity, one who receives usually feels an obligation to do something for the provider. Boundary issues usually preclude expressions of reciprocity. However, another way of reciprocating is to pass along the good deed by doing something positive for another person. A patient who receives services has a wonderful opportunity as a Compeer volunteer to "give back" by offering friendship, support, empathy, and guidance to another person who will benefit from these gifts. And so a person who feels impaired or diminished in any way as a recipient or consumer can benefit from the act of contributing to the well-being of another person, especially one who has a mental disorder.

3. *Empathy and knowledge of the mental health system:* The mental health delivery system is complex. Concepts of "split treatment" (a prescriber and a non-medical therapist or multidisciplinary treatment teams), public and private providers, in-patient and out-patient teams, day treatment, and partial hospitalization programs add many participants to the treatment team and potentially disrupt continuity of care. When one adds the components of health insurance, disability or public assistance, social clubs, residential programs, rehabilitation programs, peer support groups, drop-in centers, case management

services, among others, the patient faces a dazzling, helpful, but overwhelming array of rules, regulations, and bureaucracies. Exposure to the system and first-hand experience provide expertise unique to the patient-Compeer volunteer. This benefit enhances the effectiveness of a patient-Compeer in efforts to advise and guide his or her match through a daunting system of services.

4. *Meaningful activity:* The volunteer also enjoys a wide array of Compeer-sponsored or subsidized leisure activities to attend with his or her friend. Expansion of social and recreational activities clearly leads to improved quality of life.

Case Example

A woman in her middle years has experienced troubling bouts of depression superimposed on persistent anxiety symptoms. Antidepressants and electroconvulsive therapy have helped her to maintain both her family and vocational roles, albeit with much effort and marginal self-esteem and self-worth. As a longtime Compeer volunteer matched to a severely impaired person with a serious and persistent mental disorder, the woman has been widely recognized for her efforts (social, advocacy, empowerment, skills training) on behalf of her match. Her success with this individual, coupled with local and national recognition, have boosted her self-esteem in ways that her family and vocational activities have not. She also participates in the training of new volunteers.

Benefits to the Mental Health Professional

Benefits to the mental health professional include:

1. *Collateral information:* Compeer volunteers submit monthly reports about their contacts with their matches. The reporting volunteer will routinely describe any changes in appearance and behavior, or any concerns. The reporting form also includes a field that indicates a need for contact with the provider. Thus, the provider has yet another set of observations about his or her patient in the community as well as an opportunity for direct contact with the volunteer to gain more information or to provide guidance to the volunteer for helpful interactions. These reports, when saved, are a useful addition to the patient's permanent record.

2. *Expands/enhances the range of interventions:* Providers (except for Assertive Community Treatment Teams) can rarely participate with

their patients in community-based leisure activities, advocacy, or skills training. Case managers can provide these services on a limited basis, but the demand for case managers exceeds the supply. Family members, when available and supportive, can do the same, but the relationship between family member and patient may be too complicated to be effective. Empathic, caring Compeer volunteers, offering one or more hours per week of their time, can clearly aid patients in a variety of ways that others in the formal network of services cannot. With a Compeer volunteer, patients can practice in real life situations the skills that improve functioning and enhance quality of life.

3. *Decreased demands:* In a climate of declining financial support for mental health services, all providers face the challenge of "doing more with less." The perception of an "emergency" is experienced by the person in distress, but the situation may not meet the threshold for a clinical emergency as traditionally defined by clinicians. In spite of their commitment to availability and service, it would be naïve to believe that providers do not struggle at times with the demands and needs of their patients. It is a benefit to the provider to be able to share his or her patient's non-urgent, non-life threatening problems with others. An expanded support network means more opportunities for patients to obtain additional help and less reliance on therapists and prescribers. For members of the clinical treatment team, this translates into fewer demands for matters that may not require skilled intervention and more time to provide clinical services to others.

Case Example

A young adult woman, who has been sexually and physically victimized, has a psychotic disorder and borderline personality disorder. Her fears of abandonment and chaotic interpersonal relationships lead to frequent, intolerable distress, parasuicidal gestures, and many calls during and after traditional service hours for support. She has been matched with a Compeer volunteer in a stable relationship for three years. The volunteer and patient meet weekly for about one hour and speak on the phone one or two times each week. The volunteer has also been available for extra phone contact as long as the calls have not been excessive or disruptive (to sleep or other activities). Over this period of time, the patient, who has benefited from Dialectical Behavior Therapy (DBT), has been able to utilize both the Compeer and the treatment team more effectively for support. The volunteer is grateful for extra support and education from the treatment team. Providers appreciate receiving fewer calls while knowing the patient still receives an appropriate level of support.

4. *Becoming a volunteer:* While appreciating the benefits of the patient-volunteer match and endorsing the merits of volunteerism, I decided to become a Compeer volunteer. Over a nine-year period I have been matched with two highly impaired individuals, both residents of our local state facility at the time of the match. One has died from medical illness, and the other now resides in supervised housing. In both instances I enhanced the quality of their lives while gaining unique perspectives and personal satisfaction from these very special relationships.

Conclusion

To reach the threshold for a psychiatric disorder, impairments must adversely affect a person's social, family, or vocational functioning. Patients and their families desire success in their own individually identified goals, which typically include independent living, work, and leisure activities. Symptom relief and prevention of recurrent episodes are desirable but not necessarily the *sine qua non* of recovery. Individual providers can rarely provide all of the treatment, support services, and skill-building sessions that lead to accomplishment of patients' goals. Compeer volunteers uniquely extend and enhance the formal treatment relationship in myriad ways that are beneficial to patients and to providers. Patient and provider satisfaction underscore the perceived benefits.

Notes

1. Hogarty, G. E. (2002). *Personal Therapy for Schizophrenia and Related Disorders.* New York: The Guilford Press. Like Hogarty, I prefer to refer to the people I treat as "patients." Of French derivation, "patient" refers narrowly to "one who suffers" and more broadly to one who is "awaiting medical care and treatment." This contrasts with "consumer" from the Latin *consumere* meaning to "take," "destroy," or "spend wastefully" and with "client" from Elizabethan Poor law and Latin *clinare* meaning to "lean on" and "one who petitions for his rights."

2. Compeer, Inc. Web site: www.compeer.org.

9. Compeer: A Valuable Learning Experience

John S. McIntyre, M.D., with Ann McIntyre, M.A.

For twenty-five years, both as a psychiatrist in private practice and as chair of a large urban department of psychiatry and behavioral health, I have found Compeer to be a significant help to many patients with mental illness. Persons with serious and persistent mental illness frequently struggle with isolation, lack of stimulation, monotony, and low self-esteem. Typically they have few sustained friendships other than family members, and often they are unemployed. Contacts with others are infrequent, and when they *do* occur, the person with the illness experiences the effects of stigma, which tend to reinforce the isolation and low self-esteem. These are typical issues that are the foci of treatment. Involvement with Compeer, which directly impacts these issues, can be a major factor in the individual's recovery.

Isolation is very common in persons with serious mental illness. For those who have had relatively normal development until the onset of their illness, the isolation often occurs because the person afflicted begins to avoid usual contacts. This may be related to anxiety or at times paranoid thoughts. The "small talk" that makes interaction with others smoother becomes more difficult. Also difficulty in performing or even attending work or school leads to a withdrawal, either voluntary or involuntary, from these activities. The person with the illness increasingly turns inward and this increases the isolation. At the same time, friends and even family members may begin to avoid the person with the illness. These friends and family members often feel uncomfortable and at times frightened by the speech or other behaviors of the ill person. This is frequently compounded by misinformation about mental illness, which unfortunately is often reinforced by inaccurate and frightening portrayals of mental illness in the media. Isolation then feeds on itself. The contacts become more infrequent and when they do occur are often awkward, brief, and not rewarding.

The isolation frequently results in a lack of stimulation. Persons with mental illness, largely as a result of the isolation, increasingly engage in repetitive non-stimulating activities. They may sleep excessively, watch TV for extended periods of time, and may sit unoccupied for long periods of time. The isolation and the lack of stimulation contribute to lowered self-esteem, as the individual increasingly feels "different" and not capable of performing many tasks, some of which they still could actually perform quite well. Isolation also deprives the individual of the comfort and pleasure that results from most human interactions. The low level of new or stimulating activities decreases opportunities for acquiring new knowledge and skills.

Case Example

Frank is the younger of two children with an older sister. Both of his parents are employed and have had a generally positive, stable relationship. Frank had graduated from high school, and worked for a local company for two years when his illness became evident. Over a period of six months he became more isolated, and at times was irritable and made statements that didn't make sense. He began missing work and, after several warnings, his employment was terminated. Although he had been a relative "loner" for many years, he stopped seeing the few casual friends he still had. One weekend at home he became very agitated, seemed to be hallucinating, and with no apparent provocation began throwing objects. The police were called and he was brought to a psychiatric emergency room, evaluated, and admitted to a psychiatric unit. After a thorough evaluation he was diagnosed as having a schizophrenic illness, was started on anti-psychotic medication, and participated in the inpatient treatment program. After ten days on the inpatient unit and a subsequent two weeks in a partial hospital program, he is beginning outpatient treatment in a community mental health center. Comprehensive treatment planning includes identifying his goals and aspirations as well as his difficulties. Part of his treatment will include medication. A major focus will be preparing for his return to work or school or both and the establishment of relationships.[1]

Augmenting the Treatment Plan

For most persons with illnesses similar to Frank, such a treatment plan will result in significant improvement. For many of these individuals, however, the relative isolation, lack of meaningful relationships, and lack of stimulating experiences continue. This is the reason Compeer can be such a useful adjunct to treatment. A Compeer volunteer makes a commitment to establish a one-on-one friendship with the person who has an illness. The volunteer and his or her match-friend make plans for a monthly (or more frequent) encounter, such as going out for a meal, a movie, or a sports event. They may simply go for a walk in the park, a cup of coffee, or a trip to a museum. Or, it can be a hands-on project that the pair works on together.

Clearly these activities directly impact the problems described above as common problems that result from, or accompany, serious mental illness. In many ways, Compeer provides experiences for persons with a mental illness that are exactly what is needed for improvement and recovery. As a clinician, I can verify first-hand the positive impact Compeer has had on many patients. Furthermore, from a public health perspective, Compeer is a marvelous program because of its cost-effectiveness. Volunteers are the program's best resource. Hence, the program provides services that otherwise would be unattainable in the for-profit world.

Stigma is yet another major issue that can be influenced by Compeer relationships. As the volunteer forms a relationship with a person who has a mental illness, he or she begins to experience emotionally the reality that a person with a mental illness is fundamentally a person with feelings, wants, and emotions quite similar to those of the volunteer. The individual may seem less bizarre or qualitatively different than the volunteer had imagined. As the volunteer shares these experiences with family and friends, the circle of enlightenment about mental illness grows. Some of the volunteers are prominent members of the community and, because of their visibility and influence, the enlightenment grows even more rapidly.

Students are especially open to learning and forming new ideas and opinions. This, combined with the opportunity to have an enriched, hands-on opportunity to learn some of the required subject material, led my wife, Ann McIntyre, a professor of psychology at Monroe Community College, to begin to introduce her students to Compeer and its activities. She describes her experiences in the rest of this essay.

The MCC–Compeer Connection

What are persons with mental illness really like? This question usually arises after thirteen weeks of our college psychology class focusing on the various mental illnesses, brain scans, neurotransmitters, DSM for diagnosis, practice guidelines for treatment, case studies for a more personal approach and even some videos featuring persons with mental illness. Despite the wealth of material presented, "What are persons with mental illnesses really like?" remains a real and legitimate question. Our experience has shown that meeting people with mental illness is an effective and direct way to approach the answer to that question. So began the relationship between our classes at Monroe Community College and Compeer.

As we have seen in this book, Compeer's main service is to match clients who have mental illness with a volunteer who will spend a few hours each month socializing with his or her match. It is a friend-to-friend approach that has been most helpful for the past twenty-five years. The match program has helped the person recovering from an illness to re-enter the social world with support and guidance. It has given the volunteer a unique chance to get to know someone he or she would not ordinarily meet. Many matches have been ongoing for more than a decade, testifying to the mutual benefits of such relationships.

For several years now, the number of people referred by their therapists for matches has far outnumbered the number of volunteers available for the special long-term relationship. In order to deal with this reality, Compeer initiated a series of activities for adults and children who were waiting for a match. Thus, patients waiting for a match understood that Compeer had not forgotten them, but that staff members were searching for an appropriate match, and that in the meantime they could join in general social activities. These activities have included bingo, pizza parties, Halloween and holiday parties, ice-skating for the younger members, and rock climbing. Skill-building activities have included classes in painting, gardening, and quilt-making.

Benefits to Students

The MCC–Compeer connection has been a very successful program for the past four years. A Compeer staff member or trainee comes to four different classes at MCC that focus on mental illness. The Compeer spokesperson explains the vision of the programs, the match program, and the activities-based program, and then asks for volunteers. The Compeer representative then discusses the simple training and students fill out the application form for the organization to keep on file. There are usually questions from the students and a lively discussion ensues. For students who participate, extra credit is given.

College students are not, in general, actively encouraged to take on a one-to-one match because of the time commitment involved. Many students have responsibilities at home and at work in addition to their classroom demands. Still two matches have resulted from the classes, and there may be more still as students finish school and settle in Rochester or another community where Compeer is active. Students are in any event some of the best salespeople; if they enjoy a program and find it satisfying, they are enthusiastic and share that enthusiasm with many others.

Short of the full match commitment, students can still provide additional help. In order for Compeer to have a successful party or event, it is necessary to have other people as well as clients. Local colleges and other volunteer groups are a good source of participants for these events. Sometimes a group from a college will sponsor an event; other times it is a group from a workplace. Compeer hosts various activities, and groups of volunteers from different places will staff the events.

Relation to Educational Objectives

The educational objectives of our MCC classes are probably best demonstrated by educational activities outside of class. Invariably these experiences are the best-remembered lessons of all those taught in the semester. Even if the specifics of neurotransmitters, the difference between the PET, MRI, CT, the difference between anxiety and panic, and the research into cognitive behavioral therapy fade from students' memories, the smiling face of a child skating a full circle around an ice rink supported by two volunteers will not be forgotten. Sharing the joy of dancing to a DJ's music will remain in the individual's memory. Helping a child paint a pumpkin because the use of a knife may be too scary, or watching him win a prize at bingo for perhaps the first time in his life will stay with the student for a long time. With these results in mind, the outside activities are now required in my class.

Children

The events for clients who are children resulted in a three-fold experience for my students. The parents must bring and stay with the child and this often means other siblings are also present. The student has a chance to talk with the parent and hear how they handle their child. The parent often requires support and socializing as much as the child. Some parents are open and eager to tell a good listener about their child and any problems that may exist. They seek someone who will listen and reassure them that they are working hard for their children. They are eager for new information that might help their child even more. Other parents are reluctant to talk, because trust must be established first, and perhaps they are too busy watching their child, hoping he will have a good time. As the kids climb the rock wall or finger paint what may be for the first time, it is often impossible to tell which one is the Compeer member and which are the siblings. Each seems to be able to eat half a pizza in no time at all!

Like You and Me

What is the answer to the question posed earlier? The mentally ill are like you and me. They enjoy a good time, they enjoy the company of a friend, they are always interested in food at any event, they want to know your name and whether they might see you again. Sure, there may be some differences such as slow speech due to medication or some unusual questions, such as, what does your advocate do for you? What medicine do you take? They may have a little twitch or a pressured speech. They may start a conversation and then leave abruptly. They may be a little shyer than the average person perhaps because they have been dealing with their illness for the past four years and have been quite isolated. But basically they are people looking for a little friendship, to get out of the house, to meet new people, and to have a good time. That description sounds similar to many students I have met, perhaps because there is more that unites us than divides us. I thank Compeer for giving the MCC students an opportunity to learn one of the most important lessons in their class on mental illness.

Note

1. More details about these elements of good treatment planning for persons with schizophrenia can be found in the Practice Guideline for the Treatment of Persons with Schizophrenia, published by the American Psychiatric Association. (2004) *Am J Psychiatry* 161(2), February Supplement.

10. Volunteer Training and Motivation: The Intrinsic Satisfactions of Befriending Others, and the Helpful Elements of Being a Friend

Richard M. Ryan, Ph.D.

The theme that has emerged in this book is that Compeer is an organization based on the idea of *friendship*. The fundamental principle is that a friendship can provide a positive and protective force in the life of a person in need of social support. Yet, friendship, even with those who have experienced mental illness, is not a therapy, nor an education. A friend is an equal, a companion. Friendship is not controlling, nor intended to be guiding or directive. Rather, it consists of sharing, listening, and understanding. Friendship is also a gift; it is not done for reward or gain, but is truly voluntary. In friendships, both parties benefit without aiming to.

In this essay I discuss how several of these ideas concerning friendship and volunteerism are central to the Compeer mission, both in terms of how Compeer helps its clients, and what the recruitment and training of volunteers emphasizes. I begin by recounting the emergence of a volunteer training model within Compeer during its formative years, from the perspective of someone who played a very small role in those developments. I then turn to the core elements of the "social support" Compeer volunteers offer, and the specific aspects of friendship that make it helpful. I suggest that Compeer friendships are focused on supporting the psychological needs of the friend, promoting, that is, experiences of autonomy, competence, and relatedness. I also discuss the satisfactions that accrue on *both* sides of Compeer friendships, and the benefits that volunteers experience in supporting another's well being. The intrinsic satisfaction associated with supporting others supplies the primary "rewards" for volunteers, and they directly benefit just by being a good friend.

Compeer and the Development of Volunteer Training

Over a quarter century ago I had my first opportunities to work with Compeer as a psychologist in training. As part of my doctoral work I had hoped to do a community intervention, and was on the lookout for a worthy project. I was also specializing in motivational psychology, and a volunteer organization seemed like an intriguing climate. Through Dr. Emery Cowen, a renowned and inspirational community psychologist, I was introduced to Bernice Skirboll, the founder and executive director of Compeer, to explore possibilities at her then local, but growing, organization in Rochester.

Bernice was welcoming and open. At that time Compeer was still a small organization, barely six years old, with a few hundred volunteers largely working with adult patients from local psychiatric centers. The program was just beginning to expand to child populations, as well as to groups of the very elderly. Thus, not only were the numbers of volunteers increasing, so was the diversity of the friendships they were forming.

Volunteers at that time were being trained in a meaningful, although admittedly ad hoc, way. Once recruited, volunteers were given an orientation, usually a single session, on becoming a Compeer either by Bernice herself, one of the members of her then small part-time staff, or by a volunteer doctoral student from the University of Rochester. Thus there was not a "training structure" in place, nor was there a manual or guidebook for training.

There was, however, a consistent philosophy disseminated by Bernice and strongly shared within the organization that focused on the role of friends as social supports, whose task was to be a friend, rather than a therapist, parent-figure or authority. The important points were that friends are autonomy-supportive; they listen, share opinions, offer companionship, but do not control, direct or "therapize." They also foster relatedness: they are reliable, they convey care and warmth, and they connect by listening and understanding. Finally, there was information about how to direct friends for tangible help when that was necessary, how to set limits in a helpful way when that was needed, and how to maintain one's own boundaries, when that was needed. The thrust, however, was that a volunteer was not an entertainer, parent or a problem solver, but rather a true friend, which in itself was assumed to impact well being in a positive way.

These were excellent orienting points, and they were accompanied by up-to-date information on mental illness, community resources, and strategies for dealing with common problems. Yet, because Compeer was growing fast, it was clear that this ad hoc and somewhat informal training system needed to be formalized for the long term. Along with that, the philosophy of what it meant to be a good Compeer, and the skills and information required, needed to be articulated in a systematic way so it could be reliably passed on within the organization no matter who was in charge of training, or in what city that training occurred.

Setting Goals

Accordingly, Bernice and I decided that there were two immediate tasks at hand. The first was to develop a basic training manual for volunteers, which could be continuously refined, but which could represent the approach to social support endorsed by Compeer. This meant capturing the spirit of what it means to be a friend: articulating the essential attitudes, sensibilities and skills needed in a Volunteer. Such a manual and program outline could then be passed on consistently to create fidelity across trainers and across locations.

The second task was to create a volunteer training organization (VTO) within Compeer itself that was self-replicating. We wanted to find a way to advance volunteers with "front-line" experience in being a Compeer to take the active lead in ongoing training. The idea was to develop an "in-house" system for regularly and consistently orienting new volunteers in a context where experienced friends could also pass along their stories, wisdom and perspectives. Over the next year we experienced the challenges and joys of accomplishing both these ends.

Today Compeer training goes on in tens of cities around the world. The training manual, now published by the International Affiliation of Compeer Programs (I.A.C.P.) continues to emphasize the volunteer's role as providing a non-directive, *psychologically* supportive friendship, rather than being a physical, financial or therapeutic resource. In what follows, I look more closely at what a Compeer friendship supports, and why it yields the benefits it does.

Compeer and the Essential Tasks of Friendship

In creating the initial manual we attempted to distill and highlight the important messages embedded in the Compeer philosophy. A first assumption of Compeer is that friendship is the only resource the volunteer need provide. Although many people who volunteer for Compeer are there to help others, they are not there to help as therapists, teachers or leaders. They help by being a friend, a support, and a companion. But what is a friend?

Friends provide many things. But perhaps the most basic thing a friendship provides is what, in psychological jargon, we call *support for relatedness* (Baumeister & Leary, 1995; Ryan & Deci, 2000). The need for relatedness concerns feeling connected to others in a meaningful way. When "in-relation" a person feels significant, understood, and cared for. It means having a legitimate place in a world of others, a place where one is accepted.

A second thing a friend provides is *support for autonomy*. Friends take interest in each other's perspectives, and share in each other's "internal frame of reference." A friend does not control the other, or impose his or her viewpoint, but rather encourages the other to form his or her own choices and opinions. This concept of autonomy-support then means that a friend facilitates discussion, openness, and sharing of what is significant, without taking charge, pressuring or controlling a person to feel, do, appear or be certain ways (Ryan, 1993).

A third thing a friend does is to *support competence*. When challenges arise, a friend does not take over and simply do things "for" the other. This may solve things in an immediate sense, but it raises expectations and sometimes fosters dependence. Moreover, "taking over" can communicate a lack of trust in the other's capacity to effectively manage. On the other hand, a friend does not simply ignore challenges, or say: "too bad, fend for yourself." That represents neglect. Between dependence and neglect, however, is supporting competence. Here a friend encourages a friend to problem-solve, identify solutions and engage challenges in a way that leads to growth and self-confidence.

Research on the Three Elements of Support

These elemental supports for relatedness, autonomy and for competence, all are at the heart of the friend relationship at the heart of Compeer. Recent research, in fact, shows that in relationships where these three basic elements are present, people feel more secure, more emotionally open, and greater well being and mental health. For example, in a recent study of the benefits of emotional support, Ryan, LaGuardia, Solky-Butzel, Chirkov, and Kim (2005) looked at why individuals turn to specific partners if an emotional event occurred, and not to others. They found that people most readily turn for emotional support to those partners who are experienced as autonomy-supportive (those who won't control them or tell them what to do), who are relatedness-supportive (those who will express warmth, care, concern) and who support competence (those who will encourage them to tackle challenges; who won't demean or criticize). Moreover, Ryan et al found that to the extent that people had others to whom they could turn, and who supported these needs, the better their mental health. Of course this finding is what Compeer is based on, the idea that the emotional support provided by a friend can enhance mental health.

LaGuardia, Ryan, Couchman and Deci (2000) had college students use standard measures of attachment styles to rate the extent to which they felt securely attached with each of their major social partners, including their mother, father, roommate, best friend, and romantic partner. As one might expect, people differed a lot in how they felt about each relationship, feeling secure with some and insecure or ambivalent toward others. The researchers then explored the extent to which these social partners differed in regards to their supportiveness of autonomy, relatedness or competence. Across the people studied there was a very stable pattern: people felt the most securely attached to those partners who were most autonomy support-ive. And the more they experienced partners as providing this support, the better their relationship satisfaction and wellness.

Extending this idea in another recent study, LaGuardia & Ryan (2005) examined variations in people's emotional experience across close relation-ships. These researchers suggested that even within one's close relationships, there is considerable variability in the extent to which people feel positive versus negative emotions, and even more so in the extent to which people are willing to share their feelings. As predicted there were indeed big differ-ences in both emotional experience and people's willingness to express feel-ings with different partners. People not only had more positive feelings when with partners who were autonomy-supportive, but they also indicated more willingness to talk about *both* positive and negative feelings with those partners. In contrast, in relationships characterized by more controlling partners, there were not only more negative feelings, there was also less dis-cussion or expression of them.

These and other studies suggest that people feel most secure with, and most willing to turn to, those who support their psychological needs for autonomy, relatedness and competence. In other words, they prefer to be with—and emotionally rely upon—those who can listen, consider their per-spective, and who do not try to direct or control them. They also more read-ily turn to those who show warmth and caring, helping them experience connection and belonging. Such studies detail how being supportive of the other's basic psychological needs for autonomy, competence and related-ness fosters the highest quality relationships, yielding benefits in terms of expressiveness and wellness. This is the very kind of social support that Compeer intends: support that leads to greater well-being and growth in one's interpersonal capacities. It is precisely because so many of the people served by Compeer do not have this kind of support in their natural social networks that volunteers can make can make such a difference.

Giving is Receiving: Benefits to Volunteers

It is clear that Compeer friends benefit from a volunteer who can, in a non-controlling and warm way, provide support and companionship. But significantly, recent evidence suggests that being an autonomy-supportive friend to others may also benefit the volunteer who provides such support. For example, Deci et al. (2004) did two studies where they asked partners in friendships to rate and describe the extent to which they both gave and received autonomy-support from each other. In the first study, it was shown that *receiving autonomy support* from a friend predicted the recipient's security of attachment, over all dyadic adjustment, willingness to rely on the partner and other indexes of relationship quality. The results held for both female-female and male-male pairs. The second study replicated and extended the first, showing that the more autonomy-support one received, the greater one's positive affect, the lesser one's experience of negative affect, and the greater one's willingness to express both types of affect within the relationship. But perhaps most interestingly, results showed that *giving autonomy support* to a friend predicted the giver's experience of relationship quality over and above the effects of *receiving* autonomy support from the friend. In fact, when receiving autonomy support from the friend and giving autonomy support to the friend competed for variance in predicting psychological health, it was giving, rather than receiving, that was the stronger predictor. In other words, it would appear that in friendships it is more beneficial "to give than to receive."

Indeed, there is growing evidence that volunteering benefits volunteers as much as it does those whom they help (Wilson & Musick, 1999). For example, Thoits & Hewlitt (2001) showed that not only do volunteers have better mental health than non-volunteers, but that, controlling for prior mental health, volunteers increase in well-being during the period in which they volunteer. A review by Wilson (2000) similarly indicates that volunteers have greater self-esteem, well-being and self-reported health than controls. Meier and Stutzer (2004) in yet another recent study showed that volunteering increased life satisfaction compared to not volunteering. In addition they showed that volunteers who were motivated for intrinsic rather than extrinsic reasons benefited more in terms of life satisfaction from their volunteer activities. It appears that these gains in well being and life satisfaction are the unintended consequences of motivation that is based in the volunteer's intrinsic motivation to give, rather than outcomes of people seeking reward, recognition or self-aggrandizement.

Of course this too reflects a fundamental belief of the Compeer philosophy. It is not only the community of friends in need who benefit, but also the volunteers who serve them. By giving of themselves volunteers experience something very positive and self-affirming. They fulfill a basic goal of all humans, to connect with and contribute to the development and wellness of others. This fulfillment of a very basic need, in turn, enhances the volunteer's well-being.

The Intrinsic Motivation of Volunteers

In recent years a large body of research has developed examining the motivation behind volunteering for non-profit organizations, and more generally the motivation behind pro-social action (e.g., Clay et al, 1998; Gagne, 2003). Although the literature is large, there are a few key findings. First, by its very nature volunteering is a complex behavior, and underlying it can be many motives (Wilson, 2000). Yet, in the main, people volunteer less for personal gain, status or credentials than because of personal values, or for the personal growth they might experience. For example, Clay et al surveyed volunteers from various organizations, and showed that the primary motivations were a deep sense of values, and a desire to learn and grow through the volunteer action. More extrinsic motivations such as career advancement or helping solve one's own problems were much less frequently endorsed.

This dovetails with the observation that when agencies provide extrinsic incentives to people who volunteer, the effect is often negative. A variety of researchers have shown that interventions such as supplying volunteers with awards, making volunteering mandatory, or trying to pay people for their helping behavior, not only undermine subsequent willingness to volunteer, but can also deprive volunteers of the satisfactions they sought. For example, Frey (1997) reports how blood donors given money for donations were less likely to donate subsequently than those not given money. Because they were not "in it for the money," the reward backfired.

Why would rewards and extrinsic incentives undermine volunteer motivation? Among other reasons, as we have cited, most people volunteer to "do good"–to give something of value. Attempting to enhance this motivation through awards, rewards or constraints, however, has a paradoxical negative effect. If you pay me for what I have done, the satisfaction of having freely done good deeds is undermined, and so is subsequent motivation to volunteer. Because people are intrinsically motivated to do good, as well as to grow, it follows that organizations that help people feel effective in doing good, feel part of a community, and allow them to experience the inherent meaningfulness of their volunteer work are most likely to sustain volunteers' motivation.

A recent study from Gagne (2003) supported this view. She found that volunteers were more likely to persist if they were getting needs for autonomy, competence and relatedness satisfied in their volunteer work, and moreover, if they felt their own autonomy was supported by program staff. Because they experienced need fulfillments they also liked their work more. In contrast, those who experienced the volunteering climate to be less autonomy-supported were more likely to quit. In Gagne's perspective, it was the intrinsic rewards of volunteering, and the sense of agency behind them, that sustained volunteers over time.

Consistent with this view, Compeer offers few tangible rewards for volunteers, and little public recognition. This is as it should be. The rewards of volunteering are inherent to the relationship: They lie in the satisfactions of friendship–the feeling of *agape* that comes from nurturing another's growth. It is a side benefit that, when giving in this way, the volunteer's own well being may be enhanced.

As an organization Compeer facilitates these satisfactions, and the ongoing commitment in two ways. First, Compeer focuses not on rewards, competitions or award banquets (although these have their place in building community and acknowledging efforts) but on the quality of relationships. Second, Compeer trainers stay alert to the obstacles and barriers, particularly the formative stages of relationships that might prevent the inherent satisfactions of friendships from being realized. Staff and trainers are optimally available to listen, problem solve and sometimes provide perspective to help pave the roads to friendship, however rough the terrain. But like the support given by volunteers to friends, the help lent to volunteers from trainers must be autonomy supportive. That is, one supports volunteers' initiative and choice, their sense of connection and belongingness to the organization, and their effectiveness in the task of forging and maintaining quality friendships with those who may not always be used to them.

Summary and Conclusions

This all-too-brief discussion of volunteering, motivation and the facilitating effects of Compeer relationships can be distilled into a few succinct points:

1. The core concept of Compeer is that of *friendship.*
2. Considerable evidence suggests that certain qualities of friendship do, indeed, enhance mental health and well being, as well as openness and communication.
3. These qualities that make for a good friendship include support for the other's autonomy, (i.e., being non-controlling, and sharing in their perspective) and support of relatedness (i.e., conveying warmth, commitment and caring). Partners who support these needs foster more satisfaction, sense of security and more well-being and vitality in their partners.
4. Giving autonomy support to a partner results in greater well-being not only for the receiver, but also for the giver. More generally, volunteering seems to foster greater well-being for volunteers, especially those who were most intrinsically motivated to volunteer in the first place.

5. Volunteering is largely intrinsically motivated. It is done for its inherent enjoyments, which in Compeer lie largely in the giving of support to others, or the fulfilling of deeply held values. Compeer supports this mutually beneficial process of friendship.
6. The volunteer training organizations (VTOs) within Compeer encourage the most important qualities of good friendships. The VTOs also build upon the intrinsic motivation that drives most volunteers by placing minimal emphasis on extrinsic rewards to be gained from volunteering, and by creating a sense of relatedness (or belonging) to the organization, a sense of competence by offering relevant skills and information, and a sense of autonomy by offering non-controlling, empathic supports toward volunteer training and interventions.

References

Baumeister, R. F., & Leary, M. R. (1995). The need to belong: Desire for interpersonal attachments as a fundamental human motivation. *Psychological Bulletin,* 117, 497–529.

Clary, E. G., Snyder, M., Ridge, R. D., Copeland, J., Stukas, A. A., Haugen, J. & Miene, P. (1998). Understanding and assessing the motivations of volunteers: A functional approach. *Journal of Personality and Social Psychology,* 74, 1516–30.

Deci, E. L., La Guardia, J. G., Moller, A. C., Schneiner, M., & Ryan, R. M. (2004). On the benefits of giving as well as receiving autonomy support: mutuality in close friendships. *Personality and Social Psychology Bulletin.*

Frey, N. (1997). *Not just for the money: An economic theory of personal motivation.* Cheltenham, UK: Edward Elgar Publishing.

Gagne, M. (2003). The role of autonomy support and autonomy orientation in prosocial behavior engagement. *Motivation & Emotion,* 27, 199–223.

LaGuardia, J., & Ryan, R. M. (2005). *Variation in emotional experience and expression across close relationships and its impact on psychological vitality and well-being.* Under editorial review.

La Guardia J. G., Ryan, R. M., Couchman, C. E., & Deci, E. L. (2000). Within-person variation in security of attachment: A self-determination theory perspective on attachment, need fulfillment, and well-being. *Journal of Personality and Social Psychology,* 79, 367–84.

Meier, S., & Stutzer, A. (2004). *Is volunteering rewarding in itself?* Unpublished manuscript, University of Zurich.

Ryan, R. M. (1993). Agency and organization: Intrinsic motivation, autonomy and the self in psychological development. In J. Jacobs (Ed.),

Nebraska symposium on motivation: Developmental perspectives on motivation (Vol. 40, pp. 1–56). Lincoln, NE: University of Nebraska Press.

Ryan, R. M. & Deci, E. L. (2000) Self-determination theory and the facilitation of intrinsic motivation, social development and well-being. *American Psychologist,* 55, 68–78.

Ryan, R. M., LaGuardia, J. G., Solky-Butzel, J., Chirkov, V., & and Kim, Y. (2005). On the interpersonal regulation of emotions: Emotional reliance across gender, relationships and cultures. *Personal Relationships,* 12, 145–63.

Thoits, P. A., & Hewitt, L. N. (2001). Volunteer work and well-being. *Journal of Health & Social Behavior,* 42, 115–31.

Wilson, J. (2000). Volunteering. *Annual Review of Sociology,* 26, 215–40.

Wilson, J. & Musick, M. (1999) Attachment to volunteering. *Sociological Forum,* 14, 243–72.

PART III

EXPANSION AND EFFECTIVENESS

11. Compeer around the Country and Globe

Bernice W. Skirboll, M.S.

In 1980, Compeer in Rochester, New York, shared its model with the New York State Department of Mental Health, conducting two training workshops for the department. As a result of these workshops, five cites in New York State launched Compeer programs. As we noted in Chapter 1, in 1982, the National Institute of Mental Health awarded Compeer a National Program Dissemination Grant, which enabled mental health professionals around the country to learn the Compeer model.

When I started Compeer, I had no money for advertising, so I had to find creative ways of spreading the word about our program. Similarly, when we decided to expand beyond Rochester, I needed to let mental health professionals know that we had scholarship money available for them to learn the Compeer model and help them set up their programs. But the National Institute of Mental Health Grant did not provide money for us to publicize this. At that time, Dr. Holly Atkins of CBS *Morning News* had just aired a segment about a medical innovation that was developed at the University of Rochester Medical Center. She mentioned during the show that she had graduated from the University of Rochester Medical School. I seized upon the Rochester health connection to write to Dr. Atkins. I told her about our model program and grant, and asked if she could help. Dr. Atkins came to Rochester and filmed a segment about Compeer that was broadcast on national television.

Over the past twenty years, I've traveled around the world and have been fortunate to meet so many people who have experienced Compeer. It doesn't make any difference where they live. They may live in a beautiful city, but they hurt the same way as everyone else. They can still benefit from the care and support of friendship. People are the same all over. Friendship is truly universal.

The first of two sections in this chapter describes Compeer International. The next part addresses the chapter affiliation process and explains how to start a Compeer program. Following this chapter are case studies drawn from a variety of Compeer affiliates.

Compeer International

Compeer International (or "I.A.C.P.") represents the network of Compeer programs in the United States, Canada, and Australia. Headquartered in Rochester, New York, Compeer International provides technical assistance and program support to Compeer affiliate programs. Compeer International served more than six thousand children and adults with mental illness last year.

Compeer International was developed to serve as trainer and consultant to new affiliate programs and to support existing programs. The Compeer International office is charged with upholding the excellence of program standards. It works toward forging new directions for network programs as they grow in size and sophistication. In addition, Compeer International serves as an information clearinghouse for affiliate programs. Membership in Compeer International provides the following benefits:

- Permission to use the Compeer name, logo, and materials through execution of a licensing agreement with Compeer, Inc.
- A starter package including a manual of operations, a set of forms, multi-use comprehensive Compeer videos, and additional guidelines and information.
- Professional assistance in all areas of Compeer program management including development, public relations, fund development, and training. This is offered through written, telephone, and on-site consultation, affiliate program updates, and annual affiliate program statistics.
- A newsletter that shares successful ideas from affiliate programs, helpful information on program management, and developments in the fields of volunteerism and mental health.
- An opportunity to attend Compeer regional and annual conferences at reduced rates. Conference workshop topics include: 1) program history and philosophy; 2) acquiring initial local financial support; 3) gaining the support of mental health professionals as referral sources; 4) enlisting the aid of local media sources to help in program visibility and to attract volunteers; 5) recruiting, selecting and training volunteers; 6) matching volunteers with friends; 7) monitoring and supporting volunteers; 8) day-to-day program management; and 9) evaluating program quality and effectiveness. Advanced workshops are also offered.
- Visibility for affiliate programs through the public relations efforts of the Compeer International office and by providing representation at annual conferences and meetings, i.e. invitations from Tipper Gore and Rosalynn Carter.

- Reduced costs on various types of public relations materials and promotional items such as recruitment videos, mugs, T-shirts, notecards, etc.
- Free or low-cost specialty information booklets and packets on all aspects of Compeer including grant writing, forming advisory boards, fundraising, long range financial planning, special events fund raising, and program expansion.
- PSAs and educational materials.
- International and regional statistics on all aspects of Compeer to enhance efforts for funding, volunteer recruitment and other program resources.
- A direct, toll-free telephone line to Compeer International's office.
- An opportunity to participate in Compeer Friendship Week, designed to raise funds and gain visibility for affiliate programs.
- An opportunity to be included on the Internet through Compeer International's Web site: www.compeer.org; and,
- Support through regional representation.

Compeer International offers the following information and materials to affiliates:

- Grant writing: materials include advice on how to set goals and objectives for the grant, and how to present the grant effectively. The selling points of Compeer and a sample budget are included in the grant-writing packet.
- Fund development: materials include information about the organization, suggesting many opportunities for funding the program and how to incorporate successfully them into the strategic plan, including annual campaigns, event planning, and corporate campaigns.
- Advisory boards: materials explain how to organize and effectively manage advisors to the Compeer program.
- Recruitment information: information about recruitment strategies, including diversity recruitment. These materials include sample newspaper advertisements, materials to help target the volunteer market for recruitment, and information on specialized recruitment events.
- Compeer friendship week: this special week is held each year in conjunction with National Volunteer Recognition Week. Affiliates receive specially designed public relations materials and promotional items for fundraising.
- Video: available to affiliate programs are Public Service Announcements, a comprehensive video tape which has two versions, ten and twenty minutes, chronicling the history and philosophy of Compeer, as well as its successes and stories from volunteers and friends, and a ten-minute volunteer recruitment video which includes testimonies of actual Compeer friends.

Table 1   Compeer Organizational Chart

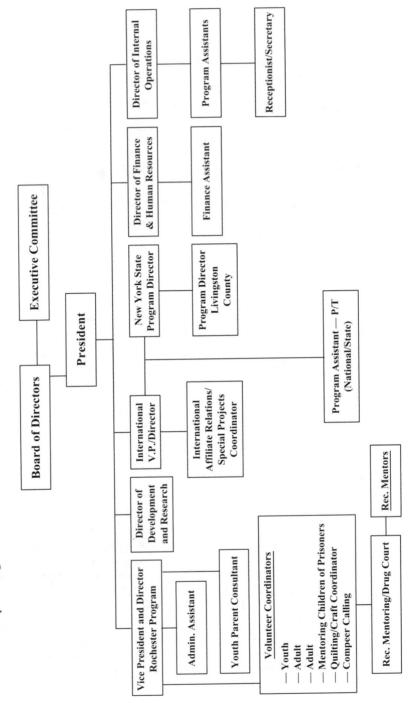

- Support materials: A variety of information is available to affiliate programs, including a comprehensive statistical fact sheet complete with testimonies from well known spokespersons, and brochures and posters.
- Design: the Compeer logo is available "camera-ready" or on diskette. Compeer International's office will design the letterhead, business cards, newsletter nameplate, posters and bookmarks and provide them on diskette, in camera-ready form, or in quick print form.

Starting A Compeer Program

When an individual or group decides to start a Compeer program in their community, they contact the Compeer International office, which advises them to adhere to the following procedures:

1. Form a Task Force

It is crucial to form a task force of people who can help identify potential advisory committee members with experience in mental health, program funding, public relations and marketing, volunteer coordination, or law and insurance. The advisory committee members should include clergy, community activists, elected officials, and consumers of mental health services.

The task force is temporary and can disband after the advisory committee is established. Task force members can become advisory committee members or serve as consultants for future efforts. If an organization or agency is acting as a sponsor for the program, members of their board may form a subcommittee to serve as a Compeer advisory committee.

Invite persons identified by the task force to serve on the advisory committee. Provide defined job responsibilities, expectations, and the term requirements. The advisory committee should then draft a plan, timeline, and budget, and identify resources to support that plan, especially in the area of funding.

A group of interested community leaders is essential to the successful management of a Compeer program. They provide guidance to the Compeer staff, assist in securing funding, recruit volunteers, and generate community awareness and acceptance for Compeer.

2. Draft a Proposal

Submit a proposal to Compeer, Inc., in Rochester, New York. Seek the advice of the advisory committee in completing the proposal. Compeer International's office can provide guidance, information, and support, based on years of experience. To insure quality programs, the I.AC.P. requires that all proposals to start a program include items in three categories:

A. A cover letter of intent stating why you/your organization wants to begin a Compeer program. Every cover letter should contain these parts:

1. Sponsor agency name, address, telephone number and executive director (if applicable)
2. The site address of the Compeer program, geographic area to be served, population numbers in that area
3. The name, title and telephone number of a contact person for the proposed Compeer program
4. Authorized signature and title
5. Program description
6. Needs assessment
7. Target population
8. Outreach/referral sources
9. First year strategic plan with goals and measurable objective to reach those goals
10. Recruitment efforts
11. Proposed budget of revenues and expenditures for one full calendar year
12. Funding sources and description of plans for future funding
13. Methods that will be in place for monitoring/evaluating the effectiveness of your program

B. Provide a copy of your application for 501(c)3 status if available.
C. Provide two letters of support from representatives of funders of non-profit organizations or local government, stating their willingness to support a Compeer program in your community.

Proposals are reviewed by the executive director or the board chairman of Compeer, Inc. If your proposal is approved, you will receive a service mark agreement, which should be signed by the authorized agent, and returned with a start-up fee. As a new affiliate, you agree to maintain Compeer's quality standards and ensure that the elements of the Compeer process are followed. The agreement authorizes the new affiliate to use the Compeer name, logo, and materials for one year. For programs determined to be an expansion of an existing Compeer program, the start-up fee is waived and only annual dues are required.

3. Establish Funding Sources

Programs are required to have a minimum starting budget, 25% of which can be in-kind gifts such as use of staff, printing and materials, telephone, travel, postage and other operating expenses. Compeer encourages a minimum staff of at least ten hours part-time initially. Plans for full-time staff should be in place for a program to grow and develop.

Developing Your Program

As your program develops, technical assistance is available from Compeer International's office to help you improve your acquisition of funding, so that your program can grow to serve more individuals. Sources of funding can include foundations; organizations such as the United Way; community support programs; sponsorship agencies; civic, corporate, church and private contributions; fundraising events; and state or county departments.

A major strength of Compeer is its flexibility to adapt to the needs of different communities. Some groups may decide to form their own non-profit corporation to make Compeer an independent agency in their area. Others are sponsored by mental health associations, community mental health centers, psychiatric hospitals, transitional living facilities, coalitions of churches, or chapters of the National Alliance for the Mentally Ill.

There are advantages to being independent as well as advantages to having a sponsor. Operating independently may provide less restriction concerning visibility and fundraising efforts. Sponsorship may offer financial security, and/or in-kind services and space. With any sponsorship, there should be written clarification about the Compeer program's ability to have fundraising and public relations efforts specifically on its own behalf.

Annual Dues

Compeer affiliates are charged an annual fee that authorizes the program to continue using the Compeer name, logo, and materials. These materials initially include the operators' manual and forms. After the first year, affiliates receive new marketing, training and public relations tools and new program development information. Payment of the annual fee also allows affiliates to attend the annual conference, and to access ongoing technical assistance such via conference calls and the Internet.

Program Evaluation

Compeer International's office is available to assist you, and will contact you by phone for a quarterly review to respond to your particular program needs. Programs must submit a written update addressing each area outlined in the initial proposal and goals for the coming year. In addition, these minimum standards should be met at the end of the first year:

1. Establish an advisory board/committee.
2. Attend at least one Compeer annual conference or have participated in at least one on-site training session.
3. Establish your training/interview/monitoring/evaluation procedures.
4. Establish referral resources.
5. Develop a volunteer recruitment plan.
6. Demonstrate financial commitment for continuation of your program.

12. Stories from Affiliate Administrators

How Compeer Came to San Diego

Shannon Jaccard, MBA

My story begins on the night of August 23, 1982. I was four years old and my family lived in Oakland, CA. I was already fast asleep when my father came into my bedroom and gently picked me up. He was carrying me over to the neighbor's house when I awoke due to the night's brisk air. He told me that my mother and he were going to the hospital and would be bringing me back a baby brother, Jeffrey.

When you have waited for what seems like forever for your family to get home all you want to do is play with them! However, that was not the case. I remember anxiously staring at my brother for any sign of movement so that I could announce to the world that he was awake and start playing with him. We have an old photograph of the first time I held my brother in my arms. My mother had piled so many pillows around me that you can hardly make out our faces.

Over the years my brother's cute looks won the hearts of all of my friends. After I reached the ripe old age of eleven, our family moved to San Diego, CA. This is the first time I noticed a change in Jeff. At first he struggled a little bit, being a second grader and new to the school, but eventually he made friends. But this little seven-year old could not shake off stress. Any type of stress–family, school, and entertainment–he took on as a huge personal burden.

As my brother grew up he became very talented in all kinds of sports from baseball to skateboarding. He was also extremely intelligent, scoring very high on the schools aptitude exams. But by his senior year in high school it became apparent that this shining star was headed for some very difficult times.

In March of 2002, my little brother was diagnosed with a mental health challenge. I watched my active, loving brother start to disappear before my eyes. A withdrawn and quiet young man began to emerge. Jeffrey was only nineteen when he was diagnosed. My family and I desperately searched for help, only to find a lack of support for people with mental illnesses. We started to feel like we had been placed in a downward spiral with no light at the end of the tunnel, and then one day I noticed something. Every time I brought a friend over to hang out with my brother his personality would light up. He would get excited about bathing and changing his clothes, and wanted to do outdoor activities. It was at this point that it became very obvious that what Jeff needed was the support of a friend. Our family started frantically searching for just this type of friendship, but once again, we were overcome by the feeling of being lost and without hope when all 'buddy' programs in San Diego turned us away. Since I knew that a friend was imperative for his recovery I decided to start an organization to fill this void.

After making the decision to start a program, my husband and I agreed that I could quit my job to give this all the attention it needed. At the time I was also finishing my MBA and was able to create the organization's business plan as my thesis paper. I started calling around and meeting with directors of other local nonprofits and was very blessed to be given so much wonderful advice. The biggest support I received was from Tod Lipka. He is the CEO of Step Up on Second, which is a nonprofit organization in Santa Monica that provides all kinds of wonderful services to persons with mental disabilities. He spent almost an entire day giving me pointers and advice. To this day, I can call upon him with any questions.

My biggest break in my quest to start a friendship program happened at my husband's soccer game. I admit that, while my husband loves playing soccer, I only half love to watch the game. So at one of his games I was going over my government paperwork to start a nonprofit organization. There was a young woman sitting next to me who turned out not only to be the wife of one of the soccer players on my husband's team, but also an attorney. Noticing the government documents she started asking about what I was doing. When I told her I wanted to start an organization that would provide friendship to San Diego's mentally ill, she asked me if I had ever heard of the Compeer program. Compeer?! As she described this friendship program, all of these wonderful emotions started rushing in. It turns out that her father is also diagnosed with a mental illness and has been a part of the Compeer program in Kansas, which is where she is from. She gave me the website and from there I learned more about Compeer and how to bring this excellent program to San Diego.

Our Compeer program started in July of 2003 and I am happy to say we are currently serving twelve clients including my brother. We have been blessed with a tremendous amount of support from other local mental health organizations, which want to see us succeed. Through another variety of wonderful connections, I was able to meet a doctor who is the head of research in Schizophrenia for the University of California, San Diego. When hearing about the Compeer program and my devotion to the mental health cause, he hired me on the spot to, not only assist with his research, but also to help provide funds so that I can continue with the development of our organization. I have also been fortunate to hold two open houses at UCSD and am becoming intertwined with UCSD Outpatient Psychiatric Services. Over time we hope to continue to cultivate a relationship with the university.

These past few months have been a trying time on my family. My father had to be hospitalized three times due to a heart condition, but is finally improving. My brother also has had a recent brief hospitalization. Even though there are days were I am angry and frustrated wondering why this has happened to my brother, I know that through his illness, I have been able to help others like him in San Diego. With every new volunteer or person that asks me about my organization, I know I leave him or her with a better understanding of what mental illness really is.

An Ordinary Life

Mary Thurston

There's this feeling of being back in grade school: the new year is starting and the first assignment is to write about what you did during summer vacation and nothing comes to mind. It was just summer as usual, but then you remember climbing trees, swimming, camping, telling ghost stories at night, hanging out at the ball field, and riding bikes. Wow! A lot did go on.

Well, that's kind of like my story. Nothing extraordinary really. Life as usual. Until I look back. I have been battling major depression and panic attacks as early as my teens. According to my sister it was even earlier than that. She periodically tells the story of when I was a child and mom would lose track of me. I could be found upstairs sleeping. It was the only way I knew how to cope when situations became overwhelming. Suicide attempts haunted me in my teens and later in life. In my early twenties, my mom revealed she knew I had an early death wish, but she didn't know what to do.

The summer of 1985 is one to be forgotten. I wasn't working, the second marriage was ending, and just two years earlier, within a three-month period, my dad died suddenly and my young niece was killed in a car accident. The blackness was overwhelming. I had two young sons who needed their mother and she just wasn't there. I wouldn't get dressed for days on end. When I did get out of bed, I just moved to the couch. Friends and neighbors stepped in. One elderly neighbor played Yatzee with my five-year-old for hours on end, keeping an eye on him while keeping him entertained. Other neighbors left fresh tomatoes, my son's favorite, on their back porches for him. He loved to think he was "sneaking" the tomatoes whenever he made a raid. My ten-year-old had an entire community taking care of him. He rode his bike all over our small town with his friends and their parents would watch over him and provide him with lunch. One friend who lived on the other side of the block would come across the back yard to see that I had gotten up for the day (being dressed didn't matter).

I didn't realize how my boys were being affected. I didn't even realize how nonfunctioning I had become. But on one autumn day, my oldest son came to me with a simple request, "I want my mom back." Only then did I realize how much trouble the boys and I were in. I called for help and started talk therapy. Medications came later and on an irregular basis. I had entered the world of "consumer," but still didn't have a name for what was wrong. My "problems" were labeled as "Adult Child of an Alcoholic." I felt that that wasn't the whole story. There was a vague emptiness that was signaling something else was wrong.

For decades I would be awakened most nights by a dream. I would be floating above my childhood crib, which was in my parents' bedroom. The blankets were draped over the side. Then feelings I couldn't name would surge through me and I would wake up shaking. In later years I tried to rationalize the dream by my belief that I was just remembering mom and dad fighting. Then one day during lunchtime at work I was reading an article in *Guideposts*. The story was of a woman who was dealing with issues of childhood abuse. Feelings came flooding to my conscience and there were three things I knew for certain. One was that I had been abused as a toddler. Two was that what I had been feeling in my dream was terror. It couldn't be named before because toddlers don't have the language to describe that sort of feeling. The third was that recovered memories are very real. I confided what I was experiencing to my supervisor, and insisted I needed to leave work immediately. Thank God he said no because he knew there was a good possibility I would attempt suicide. He kept me there for the remainder of the day and with the help of another supervisor kept watch over me. Before I left that evening they elicited a promise from me that I would call a women's help line when I got home; it's a promise I kept. Again friends had stepped in when I needed them the most.

Through all this finally came a diagnosis: post-traumatic stress disorder, major depression, panic attacks, and anxiety disorder. Medications would work for a while and then need to be switched, but at least there were other medications to try. It felt cleansing to have a diagnosis. Forty plus years of my life were now in perspective. I didn't want to wear any labels or be known as a diagnosis but now I knew what I was dealing with and with that knowledge came strength. I lost one job due to mental illness and that company's refusal to educate itself on the subject. Their only response, after months of discrimination, was to say they understood why I left.

During the time I was at home the depression and inertia became crippling. My curtains were usually kept tightly closed against any light that might filter through. On one semi-functional day I decided to walk to the post office. My neighbor was sitting on her porch and waved me over. She was concerned because she hadn't seen me out or my car moved in a long time. We chatted for a while and it was then she told me she had been watching my curtains. She was making sure I opened them every few days for when she saw them opened she knew I was up and around. If my curtains remained closed she would have called for help. Neighbors helping once more.

While unemployed I became involved with VESID (Vocational and Educational Services for Individuals with Disabilities). Through them I worked with a job counselor who was also on the Board of MHAST (Mental Health Association of the Southern Tier, Inc). The counselor and I became close as we continued to work towards the joint goal of my gaining employment. During one Board meeting it was mentioned that there was an opening. My counselor spoke up and said she knew of someone (me!) who might be right for the position at MHAST. Once more a friend stepped in.

I placed an application and later went for an interview. Although I wasn't hired for the original position, there were two other part-time openings, one requiring the applicant to be a parent with a mental health diagnosis and one for the Compeer program. I was hired for both part-time placements. The Compeer director felt I would bring a unique perspective to the program. Knowing nothing about the program I didn't understand why that would be, but I was soon to find out.

I began to earn the trust of the folks I was working for and shared small pieces of my history with them. What plagued me most was their (and my) need to be heard, to talk to someone who had truly lived and was still living their disjointed life. They needed to believe that when they shared feelings and stories about their families, medications, suicide attempts, doctors, and discrimination they wouldn't be judged or told they really didn't feel that way. The Compeer participants often express disbelief when they learn I have a mental health diagnosis. We laugh when they suddenly say I don't look like I have a diagnosis or don't act like I do or don't seem like I do. We realize its part of the stigma and lack of education we had all faced.

Until 2003 I hadn't completely realized the lives I had touched through Compeer or how much the people had touched me. My son was in the army and was deployed to Iraq early that year. It was a very difficult time for me. As I opened up to the participants about my son, support poured in. I was supposed to be here for them but the tables turned. Rarely a day ended without at least one phone call. How is he doing? Have you heard from him? How are you holding up? What are you doing for yourself? I'll keep him in my prayers. For over eleven months until his safe arrival home Compeer friends were supporting me. Even after he was home there was concern for his state of mind.

Through Compeer I'm matched with a great woman. A close friendship has grown from the match. We are close in age, share many interests (most importantly our cats!), and talk almost daily on the phone. My friend has a great memory and puts it to work for both of us. She'll call and ask, "Have you . . ." The answer is usually, "I forgot." What would I do without her?

Compeer's vision of friendship for those with a mental health diagnosis is true. I've lived it often in my lifetime. I'm proud to be part of Compeer, first as a program coordinator, second as an unofficial participant, third through my match, but most of all as someone with a mental health diagnosis.

My Compeer Experience: An Hour a Week for One Year . . . 31 Years Later

Barb Mestler

It all began with an ad in the local newspaper.

Wanted: Men and women to work for no pay for at least one hour per week for a minimum of one year. Experience with loneliness, failure, fear, loss of self-esteem helpful, but not essential. Kindness, gentleness, and patience a must. Challenging opportunity to bring another human being back into the world where we live by helping them find the love and trust they've lost.

And here I am more than thirty-one years later, still meeting with two friends for about four hours per month each and serving as program director for Compeer of Livingston County, New York: How did the power of friendship change my life too? It's an interesting story! I had been thinking about pursuing a volunteer opportunity and this "Wanted" ad sounded like something I could do. After checking with Adopt-A-Patient, a local program of the Mental Health Chapter of the Health Association in Rochester, I learned that the expectation was that I would be matched with a referred client and we would spend about one hour a week enjoying each other's company for at least one year. I was working full-time and attending evening college two nights each week. Would I be able to spend an hour a week for a year? I thought it was worth a try since it was only for a year.

My responsibility as a participant in the Adopt-A-Patient Program was to befriend a person diagnosed with a mental illness. I was to visit my newly assigned friend and provide nourishing support and encouragement. An hour a week didn't seem to be enough time to make a difference. Nevertheless, I was determined to give it a try.

I was one of approximately twelve volunteers in the program. I met with my new friend at Rochester Psychiatric Center where her social worker introduced us. We seemed to get along okay, but after just a few weeks, she decided that she didn't want to see me anymore. Nothing the social worker, program director or I could say or do changed her mind. So there I was without a friend and feeling like a total failure as a volunteer.

The Adopt-A-Patient Program Director was leaving her position, and I was approached to serve on the Steering Committee. One of our first tasks was to locate a replacement. I think I was asked to be on the Committee because it was felt that my background in business could be beneficial to the group. After many impressive candidates were interviewed, the Committee recommended Bernice Skirboll for the position. Looking back on that decision, it was the key to the astronomical growth and success of the program that evolved into Compeer.

I was determined to try my hand at volunteering once more. This time I met the person who would become my lifelong friend, "Sylvia." She had just been released from the psychiatric center and was living in a group home. She was a widow and her grown children did not live nearby. Her mental health professional felt she could benefit from having a friend because she was lonely. Sylvia was a very introverted person with low self-esteem. It was a slow process, but we became great friends. Every week we would get together and enjoy low-cost or no cost activities. No matter what we did, it was fun for both of us. We took walks in the park, stopped for coffee, window-shopped at the mall or took a ride in the car and chatted. Our friendship ended up spanning more than two decades. We enjoyed Compeer social events and Sylvia never missed an opportunity to spread the word about Compeer. We participated in many speaking opportunities including radio and television interviews. For a shy, quiet person, Sylvia did an excellent job of communicating how Compeer had provided her with a good friend and she felt much better about herself because of it.

After the first year of our friendship, we definitely continued getting together because our friendship became special to both of us. Sylvia's mental health fluctuated, but no matter how she felt or where she was living, she knew that she could depend on me to be here for her. What a special friendship we shared! No matter how hectic my days or evenings became, our time together was something I looked forward to. Our friendship ended in 1999, when she unexpectedly passed away from lung cancer.

Over the years, I volunteered for many other Compeer activities, such as serving on numerous committees, calling bingo, and assisting the staff with training sessions for new volunteers. I participated in a variety of speaking engagements. I talked about Compeer with co-workers, friends, and neighbors encouraging them to volunteer, too. I became the first chairperson of the Compeer board of directors. There were many ways in which volunteers like myself helped the program grow.

After a thirty-five-year career at Rochester Gas and Electric, I transitioned into a part-time paid position in human resources at Compeer. It was quite an opportunity to play a different role in helping the program. I was re-matched with a new friend, "Anita," soon after Sylvia's death. It was difficult for me to move on with someone else, but I knew there was a long waiting list of those seeking volunteers to be their friends. While Anita had been waiting, she had a Compeer Calling volunteer who talked with her weekly over the telephone. When we met, it was clear that another special friendship was possible for me. Anita and I get together several times each month and spend about four hours together, which is the expectation of Compeer one-to-one friends. We like to dine out, go to movies, and enjoy coffee and conversation. Anita is much more outgoing and independent than Sylvia was. She and I enjoy attending Compeer social events. We have also been interviewed by the media and have been on several television spots. Compeer is also seeking more volunteers for their many programs and we try to assist whenever we can.

My Compeer friends haven't had dramatic changes in their mental health status. But, my role as a volunteer has been to be a supportive friend. I know the friendship that I have shared with each of them has made a difference for them. However, the friendships have always made a difference for me. I feel that I've viewed the world from different perspectives. I've come to appreciate and value things differently than before I met them. I've become more patient, a better listener and my expectations about friends are more realistic.

Compeer has made me feel appreciated and valued. I have been fortunate enough to have been awarded the Paul W. Briggs Community Service Award by Rochester Gas and Electric Corporation, and to have received the New York State Governor's Community Service Award. I was also named a Point of Light under the program to honor volunteers that President George H. W. Bush initiated. I was a contributing author for *Chicken Soup for the Volunteer's Soul* in which I shared a touching story about Sylvia and me. What an honor it has been to represent Compeer!

Little did I know that my volunteer activities would have an impact on my prior and current employment. When I was being considered for a position in the Employee Relations Department at RG&E in 1980, Bernice Skirboll was contacted about my involvement with Compeer. My experiences with Compeer assisted me in gaining a position I desired at work. My part-time position at Compeer led to my current responsibilities as program director in Livingston County. I am now responsible for an entire Program from volunteer recruitment to matching Compeer Callers and One-to-One.

Volunteers with New Friends

I also have a new friend in Livingston County. "Alice" and I spend quality time together laughing, visiting, and shopping. She is a joy to be around. We have built up a great deal of trust in our two years of friendship and have many meaningful conversations. Alice says that she feels cared about and appreciates our friendship. Compeer, looking for a volunteer for one year, got more than they bargained for when I joined. But, after more than thirty-one years, I believe that I've received so much more than I have given. Compeer has become a vital part of my life. I've shared information with and gained information from, those who work and volunteer for other Compeer programs from all over the United States. Compeer has provided me with wonderful friends, challenges, fun, tears, great co-workers and an opportunity to make a difference in a program for which I provide leadership. What more could a person ask for?

Establishing Compeer In Australia

Myree Harris, R.S.J.

Compeer Australia currently consists of four programs. The Sydney program, based in the suburb of Petersham, began in 1995. This was followed by others in Wollongong, a city on the south coast, in 1998; Griffith, an inland city in 2002; and Melbourne, capital of the State of Victoria, in 2003.

The idea of having a companioning program or friendship program for people living with mental illness pre-dated our discovery of Compeer. In 1992, when the Society of St. Vincent de Paul established a NSW State Advisory Committee for the Care of People with Mental Illness, this was one of the initial goals. Over the next few years, attempts were made to design such a program, but we discovered that the task was more complex than we had imagined. In 1995, I, as president of the committee, was funded by other groups to look at clinical pastoral education programs for the care of people with mental illness and decided to investigate friendship programs also. On a trip to the USA, Katie Fear, then coordinator of our fledgling friendship program discovered the Compeer Web site. During her time in the States, I contacted Compeer headquarters in Rochester, obtaining information about the program that she brought back to Australia.

Over the next few weeks, the committee studied information about the Compeer program and decided it made more sense to adopt a model that had stood the test of time rather than reinvent the wheel. After extensive consultation, the state council of the Society of St. Vincent de Paul agreed to sponsor and support the committee's application to begin a Compeer program in Sydney. We had nothing but praise for the structure and high level of professionalism that was evident in everything the Compeer program produced. We knew that there had been a huge learning curve involved in the implementation of any new program addressing the social needs of those living with mental illness. The training programs and manuals were refined to best suit the needs of such a community service. The countless hours poured into the formation of the Compeer program would benefit us so we could most efficiently and effectively provide for those in our own community who required this social assistance. It was for those reasons we decided to apply for affiliation with the Compeer program. Over the next few months, the program successfully evolved. Initially, a lot of time went into making contact with mental health professionals, then referrals started to come in and the ongoing process of advertising for, screening and training of volunteers began. Compeer was chosen because of its structural clarity and its proven success in diverse areas of the USA: city, town, and rural areas. Over so many years of successful service provision, issues and problems had emerged and solutions had been found. Consequently, the manual is a compendium of expert advice drawn from experience. The program has a clear goal: friendship between equals, and its procedures and structures support this goal.

In 1996, I attended the annual Compeer conference, held that year in Rochester, New York. I found the training components to be an invaluable learning experience. The provision of three levels of training, rather than a vague talk fest, confirmed the wisdom of affiliating with this organization. I took this information back to Sydney and shared with the program coordinator as well as the advisory committee, which acts as a reference group for the program.

Barbara Johnson and Judith Ball succeeded Katie Fear, and Julie Hill is now coordinator. During her tenure, Judith also attended a Compeer conference in Rochester. Since 1995, Compeer, Sydney has grown steadily, with eighty volunteers currently matched. In 2004, satellite offices were established at Chatswood, in the northern suburbs and Blacktown, in the western suburbs. A volunteer training and support officer works at these locations and another assists Julie in Central Sydney.

In Australia, Compeer has been funded and supported by the Society of St. Vincent de Paul. Apart from a one-off grant from the Center for Mental

Health, attempts to attract outside funding have been unsuccessful. This is despite the outstanding success of the program. In 2000, Compeer, Sydney was awarded the New South Wales State Award for "Best Community Mental Health Initiative" by the NSW Association for Mental Health. Then in 2001, Her Excellency Professor Marie Bashir, became the patron of Compeer NSW.

Compeer in Sydney has grown from the original one-to-one adult program to add Compeer Calling and on to satellite programs in the north and west of the metropolis of more than four million people. In 2003, this program served 112 clients. Over one hundred people attend the annual dinner; many attend the annual picnic and regular coffee and chat sessions held in various parts of the city.

Monthly peer support meetings are available for volunteers. The Wollongong program—in a city of 271,000—in addition to its adult one-to-one program provides twice weekly social groups for consumers, including those on the waiting list. In 2003, Compeer Illawarra won the Australia/New Zealand Mental Health Award in the Recovery section at the Mental Health Services annual conference and in that year served seventy-two clients. That same year, at Griffith, an inland city of 25,000 people, the Compeer program served seventeen clients. The new program in Melbourne, a city of three million people, is just beginning.

Above all, the success of the program lies in the enduring friendships between Compeer volunteers and their friends who have a mental illness. These friendships have changed the lives of people once isolated and lonely. At regular social events, volunteers and friends mingle happily in the larger network of the Compeer family. Since families and colleagues of volunteers question them about this involvement, stigma and stereotypes about mental illness are broken down in the wider community.

It Takes Two

Michelle Brown

Compeer is a family of friends united for healthy minds. For the past twenty years it has been my good fortune to be the director of Compeer of Greater Buffalo. Through this wonderful program, I have met the kindest, most heroic, and giving people in my community. Compeer volunteers have helped thousands of adults and children become healthier and move towards recovery. Through the power of friendship lives have been saved, hope has been rekindled, and families have remained intact.

Compeer of Greater Buffalo currently serves 450 people annually with 30,000 volunteer hours.

Adult Program

Responding to a presentation in 1984 by Bernice Skirboll, Googie Butler, a mental health consumer and tireless advocate for people with mental illness, founded Compeer of Greater Buffalo. Under the auspices of Compeer Inc. based in Rochester, New York, Compeer of Greater Buffalo was established in January 1985 in Erie County. Due to the success of the program, Compeer of Greater Buffalo outgrew the offsite administrative structure and incorporated as a private non-profit agency on July 1, 1994. As the original component of Compeer of Greater Buffalo, the Adult Program serves consumers living with serious and persistent mental illnesses. Compeer volunteers can "follow" them as they move from one level of treatment to another. Volunteers are critical in helping people to maintain their independent living skills by providing one to one support, through friendship.

Included in Compeer's Adult Services, special volunteers are matched with elders living in our community. Compeer recognizes the unique needs of elder consumers and provides volunteers who demonstrate that friendly encouragement and caring support can truly enrich a lonely life. Recognizing this, the Erie County Department of Mental Health, in 1994, selected Compeer of Greater Buffalo, Inc. to provide what they termed "Friendly Visitors" to seniors. Equally isolating is the dynamic of elders with mental health challenges losing access to mental health professionals with whom they have enjoyed longstanding relationships. Subsequently, elders may find themselves more socially isolated and, importantly, lacking a means by which to monitor well-being. As a result, elders living with mental health challenges often find themselves without the supportive friendships that so many of us may take for granted. Trained, caring, community volunteers offer friendship and companionship.

Many things have changed in the treatment of mental illnesses over the past twenty years with improved medicines greatly increasing positive life outcomes. In addition, psychosocial interventions and community educational programs contribute to decreasing social isolation. The consumer and peer movement over the past twenty years has become a formidable force raising their collective voices fighting for social change. With one in five families affected by mental illness, families have become a dynamic movement in improving mental health treatment. True to the original program model, Compeer of Greater Buffalo has remained a constant providing friendship and support to thousands of people, young and old alike.

Mentoring Program

Changes in the children's mental health field over the past twenty years confirm the value of mentorship for children with serious emotional disorders. Mentoring has proven to be extremely successful as a treatment modality for hard-to-serve youth. In 2002, the Buffalo/Erie County Department of Mental Health, identified children diagnosed with serious emotionally disturbances who were at risk for psychiatric hospitalization or residential treatment, to participate in a new countywide program. These children and their parents chose mentoring as a needed component to their mental health services.

Responding to this need, Compeer Buffalo became the mentoring agency for these children and a vanguard in the field of mental health with the addition of a new program, Compeer for Kids, Intensive Mentorship Program (IMP). Compeer integrates our present volunteer mentorship model with a resiliency theory, expanding our services to include one-on-one skill building. Mentors are highly trained to meet the needs of children and youth with varying degrees of diagnosed mental health problems. Due to the intensity of their illnesses, these children are not good candidates for Compeer's traditional kids program, thus the need for development of a more structured and focused intervention.

Research has shown that as the level of client risk increases, so does the need to be more selective in the mentoring process. The higher the risk, the greater the demands placed on the mentor to spend time with the client, as well as an increased need for clinical supervision, and specialized training (Werner 1982). Compeer Buffalo's Intensive Mentorship Program (IMP) is an example of such resources.

Highly trained community Compeer mentors are matched in one-to-one supportive relationships, to increase developmental assets including self-esteem, social skills, and trust. Mentoring relationships promote a child's strengths such as improving their likeability, ability to get along with others, and showing empathy, thus improving their life outcomes. A mentoring relationship is different from any other one-on-one relationship because it is deliberate and designed to promote social bonding and behaviors as well as increasing life skills.

The Compeer program works. As people need food and shelter, they need a community that cares. Compeer volunteers are unsung heroes who shine their light on others and give the greatest gift of all, their friendship. Compeer does that one person at a time. The volunteers who join Compeer say they get so much more than they give. I know that is true for me also. It has been a privilege to have such a wonderful job for the past twenty years. The story below is merely one example of the hundreds that have moved me over the years.

Ellen & Joan:

Dear Michele,

My Compeer friend of many years died in March. It's hard for me to believe it. I feel the need to tell you a few things about Joan.

Joan was a kind, sweet, nice woman who suffered enormously most of her life—a life of many losses and many indignities. She loved you, the Compeer staff, and the Compeer activities, but her illness often made this difficult for her to express. You were a lifeboat in a turbulent sea of changing residences, an array of therapists, a constant turnover of roommates, rotating physicians and multiple hospitalizations. The quality of Joan's life without Compeer would be too abysmal to contemplate. Regardless of one's philosophical or spiritual beliefs, one has to wonder why some individuals suffer so much in their lives.

My relationship with Joan changed slowly and almost imperceptibly over time from my trying to be a good friend to Joan, to Joan becoming a true friend of mine. You may remember our somewhat rocky start. As you may recall, both of us were nervous and excited over our first outing. There were problems with the evening traffic and a lack of parking spaces, but finally I parked and locked the car. Satisfaction was short lived as we stood on the sidewalk and noticed the car was still running. I phoned my husband to bring a second set of keys. While we waited, we made small talk beside the vibrating car. I smiled at Joan remarking that I knew this would probably affect my marriage. I was also wondering what she was thinking, since I'm supposed to be more highly functional in this duo. While we waited shivering in the cold for my husband to come with an extra key, Joan was too polite to comment on my ineptitude! My somewhat tense husband arrived with the keys, the car settled down, and so did our anxiety. Forever after that, Joan regarded my husband as "saintly" and I never tampered with that belief. I think the experience of that incident was one of the best gifts I could have given my new friend, because she saw that if this loser can make it out in the world, so could she.

After that, Joan and I had good and bad times in our relationship often reflecting what was going on in our respective lives. I loved it when Joan laughed. It happened more often in the past few years as her psychic demons lessened. We both got a kick out of trying to convince the Social Security people that, in fact, Joan wasn't dead! Another story that she truly enjoyed involved my granddaughter, Alex, and her new baby sister, Mary. One day while I was playing with Alex, she (Alex) told me that she was calling the police to take Mary because she didn't like how she was always looking at her. Seeing my distressed look, Alex said: "Don't worry, Nana, they're not mean, and they have lots of formula." Many times after that, Joan would ask laughingly: "Is Mary in jail yet?"

Sadly, in recent times, Joan experienced considerable pain both before and after three unsuccessful hip operations. In January of this year, widespread cancer was found, and on March 17th, Joan died. Being Irish, she would have liked that date.

The lessons that I learned from my Compeer friend were that:

- Some people have very bad luck.
- Our county does a poor job of caring for our chronically mentally ill people despite its riches.
- The continued stigma of mental illness into the twenty-first century throws enormous roadblocks in the way of progress.
- Compeer enhanced Joan's life beyond measure.

There is a notion that some subscribe to that one's suffering on earth is balanced by one's life in paradise. If this is true, Joan now has first-rate accommodations and it couldn't have happened to a more deserving person.

References

Werner, E. E. & Smith, R. S. (1982). Vulnerable but Invincible: A Longitudinal Study of Resilient Children and Youth. New York: McGraw-Hill.

Sanchez, H. (2003) *The Mentor's Guide to Promoting Resiliency*. Philadelphia: Xlibris.

13. Internal Program Evaluation and Economic Benefits

Tracy Herman, M.A. and Bernice W. Skirboll, M.S.

Introduction

Monitoring program effectiveness is vital for every service-oriented organization, and Compeer is no exception. Program evaluation provides information that can be used routinely to assess a program throughout the year, examine performance in relation to previous years, and monitor services in comparison with program goals. Evaluation is a key component for organizations like Compeer to remain effective and maintain customer satisfaction.

Program evaluation serves many purposes. Through data collection, uncertainties about the program are converted to statistical evidence. Evaluation provides information to determine and improve programs that might not be functioning as expected quite yet. Findings are then reviewed, and utilized at the management level to make suggested changes to service delivery. The importance of evaluation cannot be overstated. Good leadership requires regular program evaluation as various aspects of organizational work are assessed from the staff level upward through the management level. The information that is sought and obtained reveals improvement opportunities internally and externally.

Examples of internal assessment can include communication among staff members, staff expertise in mental health issues, how information is processed (paper work, mailings, e-mails, etc.), in-service training for staff, and Compeer committees (marketing, finance, volunteer recruitment, etc.). External improvement areas include decisions about volunteer recruitment methods (public service announcements, community fairs, newspaper articles, presentations, etc.), partnerships with other organizations and businesses, and support and communication between Compeer staff, clients, volunteers, and mental health professionals, which ultimately impacts the benefits Compeer clients receive.

Program Measures and Assessment

Program evaluation has been a part of Compeer from the beginning. One method of monitoring Compeer friendships is the monthly contact between the Compeer Volunteer Coordinator and the volunteer. The volunteer submits a written report each month to keep the volunteer coordinator updated on his or her friendship. The report includes information on activities the match enjoyed together, any significant positive or negative changes in the client, and the amount of time they spent together that month. Tracking volunteer service hours is another vital program measurement. As discussed in previous chapters, Compeer aims for each match to spend four hours per month together. In many cases, we assume that the greater amount of time the friends see each other, the greater impact a client may receive. This assumption may, however, reach a plateau effect as the length of time that the friends have been matched increases. For example, friends that have been paired for several years may not have the need to meet as frequently as newer Compeer friends. The volunteer coordinator and mental health professional who is treating that particular client in the Compeer match are two resources for the volunteer when guidance or assistance is needed.

Many program statistics are tracked on a monthly, quarterly, and yearly basis to monitor the Compeer program. Our reports compare current year-to-date statistics to the previous year's year-to-date statistics in order to note substantial increases or decreases in the number of program participants. Particular reports also compare current year-to-date statistics to year-end goals. These help the staff evaluate the program on a consistent basis and they help determine whether any necessary adjustments to reach the annual program goals must be made. Aspects of Compeer that are measured every month include the number of potential volunteer inquiries, the number of volunteer interviews, the number of activations (a volunteer and client are matched), the number of terminations (a volunteer and client end their Compeer friendship), the length of match (how many months or years the friendship has lasted), volunteer service hours, and the number of clients and volunteers in each of the various Compeer services.

The Compeer annual surveys are another method of evaluation. These tools were originally developed by students and professors from the University of Rochester to evaluate Compeer's one-to-one adult service. Initially in the 1970s, only the mental health professionals completed a survey. Later, a survey was created to measure also the volunteer perspective of Compeer. Eventually, a client survey was produced. When Compeer started to offer the youth one-to-one service, surveys were also made specifically for these three perspectives, but the questions were geared toward outcomes that are relevant to children. A parent survey was added to assess the youth service.

The one-to-one surveys address client treatment goals, Compeer events, support from Compeer staff, and satisfaction with Compeer. Some questions specifically address outcomes that must be included in reports to funders. The surveys have undergone modifications over time to mirror expectations and reporting requirements of funders. Compeer's surveys underwent revisions as a result of participation in a local training exercise, Rochester Effectiveness Partnership, sponsored by the Rochester Grantmakers Forum. Compeer was selected to participate in this eighteen month intensive training for service providers and funders to enhance its evaluation knowledge and skills. In addition to reviewing the one-to-one survey, Compeer has since created additional surveys for other Compeer services.

The adult and youth surveys are distributed to all Compeer affiliates annually. Each affiliate sends the surveys to its matches and performs its own data collection and analysis. Results are also sent to the International Affiliation of Compeer programs in Rochester, where all affiliate survey results are combined to produce international statistics.

Adult Survey Results

The adult surveys assess the impact of the Compeer friendship on the client, the amount of contact between the friends, activities the friends enjoy, communication and support from Compeer staff, suggestions for improvement opportunities, and overall satisfaction with Compeer. Gender, age, ethnicity, and length of match are included in the survey to evaluate results according to a particular variable. The surveys address some of the more immediate impacts of the Compeer friendship on the client (core indicators) and other long-term, more clinical, potential impacts of the friendship (secondary indicators). For each Compeer match that has existed for at least six months, an annual survey is distributed to the client, volunteer, and mental health professional each fall to measure Compeer's impacts, using three perspectives. Every year the return rate for the three sets of surveys varies. Therefore, for any given match, Compeer does not necessarily hear from all three respondents. It may be useful then, to view the results of the three perspectives individually; however, overall results are also calculated, which combine the three perspectives, to provide a comprehensive view of Compeer's impacts.

Caution should be used when comparing results from one year to another because the client base changes frequently, with clients entering and leaving the program every month. Some long-term matches are reflected in statistics from consecutive years, but there are also many new matches each year, since the Compeer friendship is based on a one-year volunteer and client commitment. The variability from year to year is also increased when examining program outcomes on the international level, because it is difficult for the affiliate headquarters to achieve a 100% return rate from all affiliates in reporting their survey results.

The 2004 adult one-to-one survey measured the following core indicators of client functioning: feeling cared about, feeling understood, improved self-esteem, self-confidence, trust in others, comfort in social situations, and decreased loneliness. Eight hundred and twenty-six adult clients, one thousand and eighty-three volunteers, and six hundred eighty-eight mental health professionals returned surveys in 2004. The clients rated themselves highest in feeling cared about (85% reported either greatly improved or moderately improved). The volunteers also reported client improvement (90%) as the greatest in feeling cared about. This indicator was also rated the highest among the mental health professionals at 88%. Therefore, the core indicator that was most impacted by the Compeer program was feeling cared about, when comparing across the three perspectives. Other core indicators that were reported with high percentages of client improvement, across the three perspectives, were decreased loneliness (82% improvement), feeling understood (84% improvement), and improved self-esteem (80% improvement).

The secondary indicators of client functioning on the survey included volunteer goals, educational goals, employment and training goals, adherence to medication and treatment plan, engaging in treatment, reduction in hospitalizations, appropriate use of emergency services, and greater independence in living situation. Within this set of indicators, the clients reported the greatest amount of improvement in volunteer goals (67%), greater independence in living (66%), and reduction in hospitalizations (55%). The volunteers reported the greatest amount of client improvement in volunteer goals (62%). Volunteer goals were rated highest (54%) among the

Table 2   Core Indicators

2004	Client	Volunteer	M.H.P.	Overall
	n=826	n=1083	n=688	N=2597
Feeling cared about	85%	90%	88%	87%
Feeling understood	84%	87%	82%	84%
Improved self-esteem	79%	79%	82%	80%
Self-confidence	78%	78%	77%	78%
Trust in others	75%	76%	75%	75%
Comfort in social situations	75%	70%	75%	73%
Decreased loneliness	82%	79%	85%	82%
Overall client improvement	*80%*	*80%*	*81%*	

Table 3   2004 Adult Client Improvement in Core Indicators

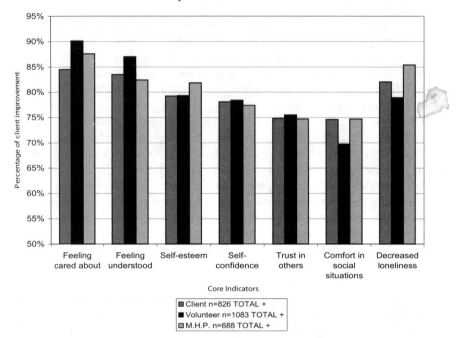

mental health professionals. When comparing across the three perspectives, feeling cared about (87%), feeling understood (84%), and self-esteem (82%) were the secondary indicators with the highest rates of client improvement.

The majority of respondents were satisfied with Compeer.

Youth Survey Results

The youth surveys assess general information that is similar to the adult surveys, except the functioning areas are youth-based and a fourth perspective is included, the parent. The areas of youth functioning that are measured include a sampling of the forty youth developmental assets, identified by the Search Institute, an independent nonprofit organization whose mission is to provide leadership, knowledge, and resources to promote healthy children, youth, and communities. The Search Institute is located in Minneapolis, Minnesota.

The 2004 international youth survey results reflect responses from 131 clients, 154 volunteers, 136 mental health professionals, and 83 parents. Fewer affiliates serve youth; therefore, the sample sizes are smaller than the adult surveys. However, more affiliates are expanding their services to the

Table 4   Secondary Indicators

	Client	Volunteer	M.H.P.	Overall
	n=826	n=1083	n=688	N=2597
Feeling cared about	85%	90%	88%	87%
Volunteer goals	67%	62%	54%	61%
Educational goals	44%	45%	26%	38%
Employment/training goals	45%	48%	45%	46%
Adherence to med. & treatment plan	64%	53%	50%	55%
Engaging in treatment	59%	N/A	50%	54%
Reduction in hospitalizations	65%	54%	49%	56%
Appropriate use of emergency services	57%	N/A	44%	50%
Greater independence in living situation	66%	54%	49%	56%
Overall client improvement	*58%*	*53%*	*46%*	

youth population, due to an effort by the International Office to disseminate the "Compeer for Kids" model. The respondents rate client improvement in nineteen function areas. Three groups reported the greatest amount of improvement in self-esteem (client: 83%, volunteers: 74%, and parents: 77%). Getting along with others was rated the highest (82%) among mental health professionals. When the four perspectives are combined, the indicators with the greatest amount of client improvement included, improving self-esteem (79%), trusting others (74%) and getting along better with others (73%). When combining all nineteen indicators, the client perspective of client improvement was highest at 66%. The parent perspective was second highest at 64%, followed by the volunteer and mental health professional (both at 62%).

Satisfaction with Compeer's youth services was at 87% or higher for the four groups of respondents.

Conclusion

Evaluation continues to remain a priority at Compeer. Additional Compeer services are also monitored through supervision of specialized volunteer coordinators and surveys, such as Compeer Calling, Skillbuilders, and

Table 5   2004 Satisfaction with Adult Compeer Services

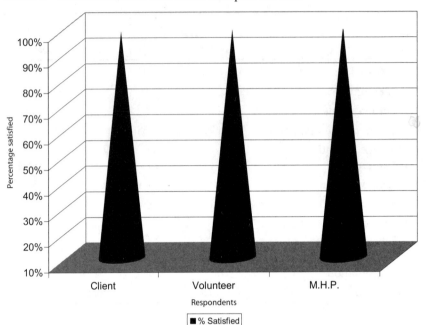

Friends for a Day. Other surveys and focus groups are used as needed to gather additional information when new programs are implemented in order to assess their effectiveness. In this day of limited resources and intense scrutiny by funders, it is crucial to measure outcome results. Without this type of data, there is no viable way of measuring the effectiveness of the volunteer on their friend. By having a multi-pronged approach to evaluation (client, volunteer, parent, mental health professional), we are getting a response from all our consumers. Consistent evaluation provides credibility to the power of friendship as an adjunct to mental health treatment.

Economic Benefits

We evaluate Compeer's success in more ways than one. Compeer not only impacts the lives of its clients and volunteers, but Compeer has far-reaching economic significance. Mental illness imposes financial burdens on the afflicted, their families, and society. These financial burdens include direct costs, which are readily apparent, such as medical treatment, hospitalizations, nursing homes, prescription costs, and rehabilitation. Mental illness

Table 6   2004 Satisfaction with Youth Compeer Services

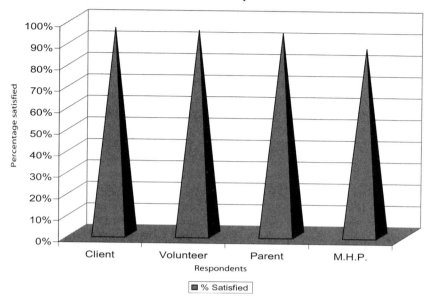

also has indirect costs that are not as noticeable at first glance. Lack of employment or underemployment leads to reduced or lost productivity.[1] This impacts the family and society in the forms of homelessness, necessity for financial support, increased crime and increased welfare expense. Experience shows that some indirect costs apply to the individual as well as to his or her family members. Family members may miss or lose employment and education opportunities, or they fail to advance professionally due to the time and sacrifices made in order to care for their loved one.

According to a recent report from the President's New Freedom Commission on Mental Health, the cost in the United States from both direct (treatment-related) and indirect (productivity loss) expenses may exceed $150 billion per year with rapid annual increases, especially in the drug treatment area. Adding to that, more than three million people are receiving disability benefits due to mental disorders. They constitute nearly 28% of disabled workers in the Social Security Disability Insurance Program, and more than 35% of people with disabilities receiving Supplemental Security Income.[2]

The website for the National Mental Health Association (www.nmha. org/access/medicaid.cfm) states that twenty-nine states cut funding for mental mental health services in 2005, and most states anticipate additional cuts to mental health services in the future. The National Mental Health Association states that untreated and mistreated mental illness costs the United

Table 7 Youth Client Improvement (major and some improvement are combined)

Respondents:	Client	Vol.	Parent	M.H.P.	Total N=
Sample size:	131	154	83	136	504
Completing homework	64%	63%	62%	54%	61%
Attending school	55%	55%	56%	49%	54%
Improving grades	55%	57%	69%	56%	59%
Community service activities	56%	55%	57%	63%	58%
Creative activities	54%	53%	52%	65%	56%
Youth programs	46%	52%	41%	49%	47%
Caring about others	73%	69%	73%	68%	71%
Trusting others	75%	71%	67%	82%	74%
Getting along better with others	75%	72%	71%	74%	73%
Personal responsibility	70%	65%	71%	59%	66%
Avoiding alcohol/drugs	42%	50%	47%	37%	44%
Making good choices	78%	68%	73%	69%	72%
Resisting negative peer pressure	74%	67%	67%	62%	68%
Empathy/sensitivity	67%	62%	66%	59%	64%
Resolving conflict non-violently	73%	61%	62%	56%	63%
Improving self-esteem	83%	74%	77%	80%	79%
Sense of purpose in life	66%	63%	73%	69%	68%
Seeking healthy lifestyle	65%	61%	70%	62%	65%
Optimism about future	74%	68%	68%	67%	69%
Avg. for each group of respondents:	66%	62%	64%	62%	

States $105 billion in lost productivity, and $8 billion in crime and welfare expenditures each year.[3] Medicaid cuts result in long-term consequences for patient health and government budgets because they lead to higher hospital and primary care costs, greater reliance on correctional facilities and welfare, and other costs to society such as lost productivity and suicide.

The Compeer Response

Compeer addresses the challenges of decreased funding and soaring mental health costs by providing creative and cost-effective services. Compeer

Table 8   2004 Adult Client Improvement in Secondary Indicators

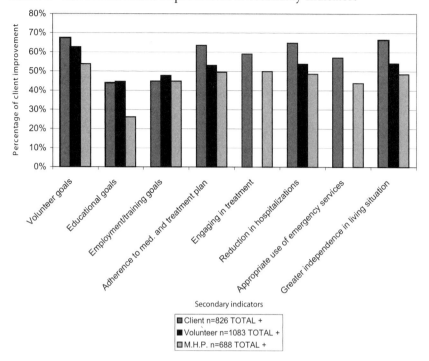

volunteers provide a direct service to mental health consumers as a free adjunct to therapy. Compeer friendships help to trim the financial burden by reducing the need for traditional and costly health care services such as initial hospitalizations, re-hospitalizations, and emergency services. These savings result in part from the increased compliance with medication and therapy goals that Compeer clients achieve. Savings also occur because Compeer friendships help clients increase their ability to make appropriate choices and decisions. This results in fewer trips to emergency rooms and fewer hospitalizations.

In 2003, mental health professionals overseeing Compeer matches internationally indicated that after being matched with Compeer volunteers, clients experienced positive impacts in the following areas: 49% reduction in psychiatric hospitalization, 41% improvement in appropriate use of emergency services, and 44% improvement in adherence to medication and treatment plans.[4] Psychiatric hospitalization costs can range as high as $200,000 annually. The cost of a Compeer friendship, by comparison, averages $1240.

Compeer also affects the economics of mental illness by raising the self-esteem of the clients. Higher self esteem results in greater achievement of clients' education, training, and employment goals. And, Compeer addresses more than self-esteem. Volunteers work directly on improving clients' functioning as productive citizens by helping them set realistic goals and then by encouraging and assisting them to reach these goals. When mentally ill citizens acquire education, procure and sustain employment, obtain affordable housing, and contribute to society, the economic burden of mental illness decreases for everybody.

Notes

1. 2000 Surgeon General's Report, chapter 6. Retrieved from www.surgeon-general. gov/library/reports on December 16, 2004.

2. Retrieved from www.nimh.nih.gov/about/2005budget.pdf on August 23, 2005.

3. Fiscal Year 2005 President's Budget Request for NIMH. Retrieved from www. nmha.org/access/medicaid.cfmretrieved December 16, 2004.

4. 2004 International Compeer Survey.

14. Stories

A Journey from Client to Volunteer

Susan Koslosky

When I joined Compeer in December 1992 I was very insecure. I was living in a state-run residence for people recovering from mental illness. My Compeer volunteer was a young woman whom I will call Jill. She was very good for me. We got together often and also spoke on the telephone. We were together until December 2001. Compeer was very important to me and for me. During those years with my match I overcame many obstacles. I gained confidence and good self-esteem.

Compeer also gave me the confidence to go to a training program in Syracuse, New York, to become an advocate for people with mental illness. Over the years after the training I spoke on many occasions at different functions about mental illness.

I learned that I could be anything I wanted to be as long as I believed in myself. Compeer was a big support for me and I eventually went to college. I studied to become an office technologies technician. I studied computer programming and learned many things that would help me get the skills I would need to obtain a job. In May of 1999 I graduated from Mohawk Valley Community College with a certificate in office practice. My volunteer was there to watch me graduate just as she was there the day I got married in 1994. It was a great day; a day I would not have had if I hadn't had my friend Jill. In December of 1999 my friend Jill and I parted, though we continue to stay in touch.

Shortly thereafter I became a Compeer volunteer with the goal in mind to give to someone else the same support in her life that Compeer had given me. My first phone match was a woman whom I will call "Sheila." She was suffering from depression, a lack of confidence, and low self-esteem. I talked with her from June 1999 until December 2001. I felt great about this. It was a chance to learn about others beside myself. When we ended our match together, I felt confident that Sheila would do well.

Then in May of 2002, I became a one-on-one match with "Stacy." Stacy was an insecure young woman who was afraid to do things because of low self-esteem. In December of 2002, I had to end the match because I was unable to give her what she needed. Her needs were more than I could reach at the time. I was working a full-time job by this time and our schedules didn't coincide with each other. I felt Stacy would benefit from someone else.

During the years that I befriended the first two women I also gained more confidence from Compeer to work at a successful job full-time. This is something I had not been able to do in over fifteen years. I was always in and out of the hospital, so life was too chaotic. Compeer brought me a sense of structure, and with its support I was able to become a successful person.

In June of 2003, I was matched with an older woman. "Janet" is a woman who is unable to get out due to her health. She has become more open and we speak on a weekly basis. Becoming a volunteer over the years has also given me such a great sense of self-worth and the confidence to take on new challenges in life. Compeer has taught me that with love, support, understanding, a friendly, kind heart, and someone to believe and care about you, you can achieve anything you want in life.

Recently I moved from New York State to Virginia. It has been the biggest change in my life. I have always lived in New York. Compeer supported me then, and it is still a big support. I still speak with my match on a weekly basis. Janet and I are still close even though she is in New York and I am in Virginia. I find it a great confidence booster that I can still be there for her.

Compeer has given me so much that words cannot describe the gratitude and respect I have for this organization. This program will always benefit those who need support because Compeer shows you that you are just like everybody else–you just need a special friend to bring out the best in yourself. I hope to stay with Compeer for the rest of my life–that's how much this program has done for me. I want and need to belong to something that works and Compeer does. I will always be indebted to this organization for the rest of my life.

God bless everyone that is involved with Compeer because anyone who is involved believes in himself or herself and those they are friends with. My gratitude for this program is overwhelming. I hope I can continue to be involved into the future.

Sharing the Load

Ted Nixon

In 1988, my life began to change. I had been doing the same thing in commercial radio since college, and my professional life held few surprises. My personal life was another matter. My mother contracted a rare form of cancer, and, rather than go through the long and uncertain treatment process, she decided to put her affairs in order. Her illness and impending death were a great shock to me. I was the youngest of three boys and, I believe, her favorite. The aftermath of her death in the summer of 1988 left me spinning out of control, and in 1989, I saw the end of my well-ordered professional and personal life.

I was talking with a friend in 1989, and I asked him what I could do to get out of the depression I was in. He suggested helping another struggling person and gave me the name of Compeer. I honestly didn't know anything more than the name when I made my first call, but I quickly learned, in a personal interview, what the agency was all about. I was approved and given several potential friends to choose from. I picked a man named Tim, a year or so older than myself, and we got together for the first time a week later.

One of my political heroes likes to quote the expression, "A journey of a thousand miles begins with a single step." That is how my relationship with Tim has been. We have been together for thirteen years. I have seen him as often as twice a week and as seldom as twice a month over that time. The constants in our relationship have been our ability to enjoy each other's company, to be honest with each other, and to accept each other's mental frailties. By the way, that is a two-way street.

Tim has been diagnosed schizophrenic, but he is one of the lucky third that is high functioning, and over the last thirteen years he has held a number of jobs. He is not currently working, but makes noise about it periodically. Tim has been on a number of combinations of medications and his current regimen seems to be working well. What has remained the same over the last thirteen years is Tim's absolute delight in having me for a friend. When I call him or when I see him, he is genuinely thrilled to hear from me or see me. He knows that he can count on me to be there for him, and I know I have a life-long friend whose loyalty and steadfastness will never be in question.

I have experienced the same thing myself. When I was at my lowest point, after the death of my mother, I had many friends who came to my aid. Many of those friendships have deepened over the years. When friendship is built on mutual respect and understanding of mutual fallibility, the friendship lasts and weathers all sorts of storms. That is the way it is with Tim and me. We know each other so well. I have shared with him my mental health challenges, my life challenges, and the things I care about. Tim has shared his life with me. I got to know his Aunt Maddie, who died at age ninety-two. We have visited the cemetery where his parents lie. We have looked at pictures of Tim as a teenager and talked about his fears and aspirations.

Tim is someone I would never have met without Compeer, and I would have been the less for it. I would have missed the enriching experience of knowing, helping and being helped by an unusual, courageous human being. It's hard to remember when Tim wasn't in my life. He's one of the family. As the song says, "he ain't heavy, he's my brother." In fact, he does the carrying as much as I do.

Me and Compeer

Larry Raub

I used to be a person with nothing to do or places to go. So much of my time was spent staying in my apartment: lots of TV-watching with little interest and feeling lots of boredom and unhappiness. I felt as though I was here in the world for something but had nowhere to go and have fun and meet others. That all changed when I first heard about Compeer about ten years ago. At that time I was uneasy about such a program. My first thought was that it was something for other people, not for me. I had no problems. But after about one week of thinking it over, I decided to become a Compeer member. It was very hard at first to talk about my problems and troubles. In general, I am not a talker, more a listener. But that got better over time. With help from my doctor and staff at Compeer, I soon felt more at ease with others who wanted to help me. It took a somewhat strong effort on my part to seek their help. Take it from me—I know now that I needed help in more ways than one! Having someone to talk and listen to me and my problems makes my life a little more bearable. Going into the hospital many times for treatments is no piece of cake. Time in the hospital, different kinds of pills, and being able to talk have all helped me feel somewhat better if not totally cured. And things have improved over time. Talking to someone who cares to listen to me and understand my problems helps me to feel better about myself. I think now that I am a better person in life. In the beginning I had a Compeer staff member call me once a week. I looked forward to hearing from her because without her I had no one to express my feelings to or talk about how my workdays were going. Her phone calls were the best—and that goes for her, too! I cannot say enough about my Compeer caller and how kind and caring she is.

A little over five years ago my life changed for the better again when I was first introduced to my Compeer match, Frank. He is a very intelligent man with lots of knowledge in helping me solve my problems. He reminds me a little of a doctor I used to see in the past—very caring and understanding. With him I feel I can talk openly. He is a good listener and a great source of knowledge about everyday concerns. When I confide in him about something that is upsetting me, he usually finds a way to help me look at the problem and solve it. We go places and do things together that I never did before. Having him around is almost like having another parent. Of course, I still love and care for my own parents very much. But there is something about Frank that I am very comfortable with. Having a friend in my life is everything to me. In my early years of life, I had very few friends. I was an outcast at school and had little social contact with others as I was growing up. All that has changed now because of Frank and Compeer. I know now that I have someone to talk with and go places with. I am enjoying a better life through friendship and Compeer. I would like to say "thank you" to all who made this possible for me—my doctors, Compeer staff members, and my friend Frank. Without this help, I wouldn't have people and places to go and see. Compeer is a great way to make friends, and I would encourage anyone out there who needs it to join the program as soon as possible.

A Friendship for a Lifetime

Debra Bonsignore

It is June of 1994 and I was sitting at Friendly's, across the table from a very pretty girl with huge hazel eyes and long dark hair. "Sandi" was ten, almost eleven. Sandi is my Compeer friend and this was our first get together. Sandi was not saying a word.

I had spent several weeks getting to this momentous occasion. The process started with an application to become a Compeer volunteer, followed by an interview with a volunteer coordinator. The coordinator had reviewed my application and checked my references. I had gone through the volunteer training, had a "match" meeting and chosen Sandi as my Compeer, met with her teacher and her counselor at school and also with her parents. I had passed muster with every person necessary to finally get to meet Sandi and here I was, totally convinced that the one person I wasn't going to "pass" with was Sandi!

I come from a very boisterous Italian family, where love and chaos reign in tandem. I didn't have much experience with a quiet, shy, introverted little girl. However, having been in the sales and marketing field for many years, I remembered that the best way to draw someone out was to ask them leading questions about themselves, questions that required more than a yes or no answer. So, I tried . . . to no avail. Even those open-ended questions resulted in no more than a one or two word answer. I realized that wasn't working. So

I tried something else that I know how to do pretty well. I talked! And I talked and talked and talked. In the little time we were together at that first meeting, Sandi knew more about me; what I did, what I liked, who my family and friends were, than people who had known me for years!

When I dropped Sandi off, I knew that this first meeting was no great success. I also thought she didn't have any kind of fun and I was hoping that she would not "fire" me. Thankfully, she didn't. I found out much later that she really liked me a lot, right from the start and she had enjoyed our first visit. She told her family all about it. I guess that proves that things aren't always what they seem. Lesson learned.

Sandi and I have been friends now for more than ten years. We have done many things together. I taught her to roller-blade, many years ago. Now she skates circles around me. We went on picnics and to the movies, we went to Marineland and Seabreeze Amusement Parks, we did crafts and made jewelry, we went shopping. Sandi and I went to the theatre and attended Compeer events. I cannot even begin to list all the things we have done together, over these past ten years. And we always ate! We discovered early on that eating was one of our common interests, so whatever else we did, we always managed to eat! It took a while for our relationship to grow to where we could easily and comfortably sit across a table and just share food, but now it is one of our favorite things to do. It gives us a chance to catch up and re-connect.

As time went by and we were having fun doing things, Sandi also started to open up and talk. She told me about herself and what was going on in school and with her friends. She met my family—my parents, my siblings, my nieces and nephews. Everyone loved her and Sandi became an extension of my family. Sandi attended all sorts of sporting events to watch my nieces and nephews play, she came to family birthday parties and special events. Sandi has a natural connection with children and my nieces immediately gravitated to her. We had pajama parties together; a bunch of giddy girls doing hair and makeup and watching movies until we couldn't keep our eyes open. Sandi has also met my friends and "hung out" with the big kids, too.

It has been an incredible experience to watch this shy little girl grow and change over the years. In April of 1999, I was honored with the Compeer Youth Volunteer of the Year Award. Sandi, who at first meeting didn't say more than one or two words at a time, stood up in front of a roomful of people and gave a speech she had written herself, sharing thoughts about our relationship. There wasn't a dry eye in the house.

A couple years ago, I was privileged to share Sandi's high school graduation ceremony with her family. I am still not sure which one of us cried more, Sandi's mom or me. I don't think I could have been any more proud of her if she were my own daughter. Sandi is now in college, pursuing her dream to teach young children. She works in a day care center and has gotten her driver's license and her own car. This young woman today is light years away from that introverted, quiet girl sitting across the booth from me at Friendly's all those years ago. Sandi today is articulate, self-assured, outgoing and confident.

Over the course of our friendship, things have not always been happy and light. There have been several occasions over the years when Sandi has been faced with sad and challenging events and she has called on me. We have talked and laughed and cried and I believe that our friendship has not only applauded and supported her through the good times, but also helped her over the rough ones.

I believe that the power of our friendship has helped give Sandi a secure and loving place to blossom and grow. There is no judgment here, only unconditional love and friendship. I am not her teacher, her counselor or her parent. I am her friend and confidant. I believe that to be the biggest blessing of a friendship like ours. Knowing that there is someone out there who you know cares about you deeply, whom you can trust and count on, no matter what. It is not a one-way street, either. I know that I have benefited as much from this friendship as Sandi has. It has given me the opportunity to do lots of fun and interesting things. It has enabled me to share my experience and knowledge and to learn new things as well. My relationship with Sandi has challenged me, uplifted me, and taught me the valuable life lessons of patience, tolerance, respect and trust and the power of love and commitment.

Sandi and I will always be friends. This relationship has transcended our initial Compeer introduction and become a significant and integral part of our lives. I know that it will continue to grow and change as all friendships do over the course of many years, but it will always be there. I am grateful to Compeer for my friendship with Sandi. It is one of my life's greatest gifts.

William Koegler

My daughter Sandi was born a two pound nine ounce preemie, one of a set of twins. After about sixteen hours, her sister, Tess, returned to her creator. After another two months, Sandi came home. Her survival had been a challenge and she suffered through numerous bouts with apnea and bradicardia, which in the long run did some minor damage to her developing brain. At age two and a half she lost her mother to drowning. Her little brother is a non-verbal autistic boy whom she adores and watches over. At around four or five I was remarried to a wonderful woman who took right over as a true "mom" to the kids. Sandi and her best friend Emily (now her sister) had a lot to do with that.

As Sandi grew we noticed that she was very shy and quite withdrawn. You could tell that the pressure of school and not quite fitting in was beginning to take its toll on her. She is a bright girl, and a very compassionate girl, but some of her learning skills, especially math, science and reading fell behind. Sometimes she just didn't catch on to things as fast as her classmates did and so ended up in special education.

We were also doing a home program with Zachary at the time. So with three children in the home and volunteers coming in and out, Sandi was starting to get a little lost. Then Compeer and a dear friend, almost part of our family, Debra, came into our lives. Compeer saw that Sandi, and the family, could use some help. They gave us a way to give Sandi that little extra boost she needed to soar. Debra and Sandi became the best of buddies. Sandi became as much a part of her family as she did of ours. In Debra's family, Sandi is one of the grandkids and some of the kids treat her like she is one of the aunts.

Over the years they were always off doing something: walking for breast cancer, rescuing greyhounds, photography in the park, shopping, sleepovers, eating (lots of that), and mostly laughing. I've lost track of how long they have been together, but Sandi will be twenty-one this summer and is a sophomore in college studying to work with pre-school children. She is healthy, confident, outgoing, and simply a wonderful young woman. You may feel I am biased since she is my daughter, but ask around the Compeer office. I think my opinion will be verified.

Sandi and Debra are now thinking about volunteering as a team with another Compeer candidate. Together they promote Compeer. If you are reading this because you are thinking of helping out Compeer or becoming a volunteer, I urge you not to hesitate. Your time, your donation, your prayers, will help light the way for another girl or boy like my Sandi to overcome the rough road they started down and lift off and soar into a bright future.

Thank You for Compassion, Compeer!

Loyd Peck

How has the Compeer program assisted me in getting my life back together, even though I am mentally disabled? The program taught me that I am not alone. Isolation is the worst thing that can happen to the mentally ill. Isolation very often leads to death, while companionship leads to revival, the pure thrill of living. Volunteer companions in the Compeer program eagerly demonstrate that they care about their disabled friends, and slowly, but surely, return that glimmer of a grin back to their once distraught participants.

Participation is key. Allow the friend to actively experience everyday challenges again and he or she begins saying, "no problem." When the ill people are locked up inside so they cannot experience a sense of joy, then depression flattens their ability to express themselves without fear of consequences, real or imaginary. If you can get the disabled person to function, even on a limited scale, it is a brave start. If you can get them to feel better about their activity, all the better. Remember that your disabled friends are very likely to be sensitive to the point of over-correction for the purpose of feeling safe, or with the "in crowd." If they don't feel comfortable offering a different opinion, they won't. But if you can get them to let down their guard a little, you'll most often find them to be articulate. Speaking works pretty well, writing works better, because it organizes one's thought processes, so one can communicate in sentences and paragraphs better than just disjointed words and tired phrases. If you can get the disabled friend to think and not just react, he/she is well on the way to recovery.

Volunteers, always remember to inspire a sense of mutual trust in your relationship with your Compeer friend. Some level of deceit may have been responsible for the friend's health problem in the first place. But if volunteers and friends feel good about doing activities together, that is most of the battle. An open relationship can be risky, but can also be the most rewarding. Developing trust takes time.

The best way to experience a rewarding relationship is to "jump right in." The feeling of exuberance is what both of you are looking for. Not preplanned, correct to every syllable, perfect unity, but a good measure of spontaneity. It is that way here in Alaska. We call it the "Alaska Spirit."

The last thing a Compeer friend is looking for are constant reminders that he or she is sick and needs to be in the hospital or attic all their lives. This is the problem with stigma. Whatever their disability, those who are in a wheelchair or dealing with whatever handicap hear the uninformed public automatically blurt, "What is he/she doing out in public? That person needs to be in the hospital." Over and over again. The words. The scorn. The fun made of. The persecution. The critical remarks. It gets old. I know, after hearing it for twenty-eight years. But here is what the volunteer is there for. To reassure his or her friend that the remark is uncalled for, and to continue their activity. Thank you my friend for your understanding!

So, what do my volunteer companion and I like to do for a weekly activity? He comes over on Sunday, midmorning, to my house. I pour us both a large glass of grapefruit juice. We watch pro-football and discuss the week's news. Then "Rocky" or I ask, "Who won last week's Championship of the World?" To which the other of us replies, "Rackum!" We play the best of three on my well-used pool table. In the summer we drive over to nearby Campbell Creek, where we watch salmon spawn, and keep an eye out for grizzly bears.

From Client to Board Member

Nancy Jepsen

Some twenty-five years ago, I was taking an evening class when a recruiter came in to explain the Compeer program to the students. It immediately interested me. However, I did nothing about it for another five or six years.

Then I received a notice in the mail that a recruiter from Compeer was coming to an organization I belonged to–The Brain Injury Association–and I made an effort to attend that meeting. Afterward, I made a point of talking to this woman and followed-up with an appointment to see her in her office at Compeer.

I wasn't sure if I would be capable of being a good volunteer as I had been diagnosed with mental illness as a teenager and had periodically experienced depression. I decided to be matched in the program first as a client and see if I felt capable of learning to become a good friend.

My therapist supplied the necessary paper work and I was matched. This match was very successful for about five years until my mother passed away and my needs changed. I said I no longer needed a volunteer. Shortly thereafter, I found that life was becoming difficult with my grief and caring for my elderly father after he had a stroke. I asked to be referred to Compeer with a specific request. I wanted a friend who had experienced death and had some understanding of the stresses of eldercare. My friend and I were almost a match "made in heaven." To this day we have never had a cross word, but we have had plenty of laughs.

As I became more comfortable and confident in my Compeer friendships, I decided that I might have something to offer another consumer, particularly in the area of head injuries–as I had learned from my own experience. Soon thereafter, I became a volunteer with another head injured person, whom I will call "Ellen." Ellen was a gunshot victim who had been in the system many years and had "fallen through the cracks." She had been placed in a sheltered workshop, which she hated. At first this relationship was very difficult for me as she saw my role as one of a taxi driver, not as a friend.

The Compeer staff provided me with support through this period and I was able to work with Ellen and show her that friendship was based on mutual interests and caring. Without this support, I might have given up, but after the first year, things in our relationship grew. Ellen had a son who was in the youth program and his friend provided money for all their outings. I taught Ellen that it was better to invest oneself into the relationship and not look at friendships for what our friends could do for us.

I was diligent in reporting the problems as well as her achievements to Ellen's therapist through the monthly Compeer reports. I mentioned that she was unable to make change when handling money, and to read. These things caused problems with her children and her self-esteem.

Eventually, Ellen was recommended for a training program, which helped her to improve her skills. She also became employed at a large local grocery chain arranging flowers. Ellen loved doing that and was more self-sufficient with her new skills. She now had more friends because she had a realistic expectation of what friendship is all about.

Becoming a volunteer involves quite a bit of time and self-sacrifice, in that you have to be interviewed by the Compeer staff for your suitability to this endeavor. A background check is done and a prospective volunteer is expected to meet the consumer's therapist after completing several sessions with the training program. For any former consumer, this is a very big step that can be rather emotionally charged. However, it is a growth experience that leads to an increased feeling of self-worth and a sense of accomplishment.

During my involvement with Compeer, I became very interested in the program and started to do a little fund-raising for the program, with the help of one of the supportive staff members. I had always said that I would never ask anyone for money. Since I believed so strongly in the need for the program, and quickly understood the need for money to offer quality services, I was now doing what I said I never would. I even won a leadership award from the Compeer board for having raised the most money one year.

The Mental Health Association offered a board-training program and I was invited to attend. After graduating from that, I was offered a position on the Compeer Board. I was always a shy person who was somewhat afraid of authority figures. Yet, I found myself comfortable on a board with others who had excelled in various walks of life. I somehow knew that I had something to offer. My life's experience gives me a very unique perspective on the feelings of others more like myself. I am nearing the end of my second term on the Compeer board and it has been a growth experience for me as well.

The Place I Was Meant To Be

Jeff Shair

Compeer believes in the concept of being involved in the community and being with friends, a philosophy that I value. My experience with friends and feeling comfortable in going places in Philadelphia, made me want to build those supportive connections with my companions at Compeer. But it took me a while to get to this place in my life.

I have been a consumer for over thirty years, being diagnosed with schizophrenia a month before my high school graduation. For several years after that, I was lonely and isolated, and basically only communicated with my mother, father and brother, Paul. It wasn't until I became a client at a mental health day program in Philadelphia that I got the support I needed. My counselor persuaded me to go out on weekends with friends I met at the program. These friendships were a tremendous help. I soon found myself becoming confident and happier.

It was the early 1990s and I was doing very well teaching and taking courses at the Community College of Philadelphia. I had also started volunteering at Compeer. I know firsthand how it feels to be lonely and isolated, and I wanted to be able to help someone overcome these feelings. I believe having friends and doing things in the community builds confidence and motivation, and helps people to cope with stress.

Then, I had another setback. The medication that had helped me live so well consequently did damage to me. I developed Tardive Dyskinesia, a movement disorder that affected my walking and breathing, and caused me to grimace frequently. This new affliction weighed heavily on my self-esteem.

In 1993, my father died. He was the last of my immediate family to pass away, as my mother and brother, Paul, died several years earlier. Being a volunteer at Compeer helped me to feel less lonely. My companion, Bob, and I got along great from the start. We enjoyed movies and baseball games. I also introduced Bob to folk music and we saw many concerts together. I fondly recollect the time Bob suggested we go to a Moroccan restaurant downtown. That was an experience that I will never forget! We had to knock on the door to enter the restaurant. We sat on the floor as we ate a seven-course meal with our hands. Then a very tall waiter poured the hot tea into a tiny cup on the floor. The whole experience was mind-blowing!

One of the most meaningful and poignant times I had with Bob was when he invited me to go to his A.A. meeting. I heard him give a very emotional testimony about his recovery. I started to develop confidence in my ability as a volunteer and felt good about the strides Bob was making.

I also met several friends, Kristen, who was volunteering at the time, and Ruby, Vicki, and Linda, who were Compeer staff members. They all believed in me and constantly were telling me how much I meant to the program. Kristen has been a dear friend for more than twelve years now, and I probably would not have had the good fortune of meeting her if I wasn't involved in the Compeer program.

In 1994, Vicki and Linda asked me to write for the Compeer newsletter about places that volunteers and companions could go based on my outings with Bob. I had never published anything. I named my monthly column "On the Town." Each month I would write about a museum, movie, play, concert or restaurant. I had fun doing the articles for the column and it was the beginning of my journey as a writer–a journey I was told I would never make.

Writing the column made me recall taking aptitude tests at Jewish Family Service when I was in high school. The counselor called me into his office to discuss the results. Candidly, he told me I would never be a writer. This remark seemed odd to me because I never planned to be any kind of writer in the first place. I guess he was just trying to be honest, but he was obviously wrong. I would like to tell that counselor today that I went on and became a staff writer for Community College and Temple University.

With increased confidence in my writing ability, I took a creative writing class. I was amazed at my creativity in that class and the diversified forms of writing I was able to do. One evening before class, I was looking at the bulletin board when my creative writing teacher came by and saw me looking at an ad for the school newspaper, *The Student Vanguard*. He said, "Jeff you are a natural" and he persuaded me to go to the Vanguard office and see if I could join the school newspaper. After reviewing my articles from my "On The Town" column, they selected me to be a movie critic for the paper. I continued to do movie reviews for the college the next semester.

My cousin, Joan, noticed my developing writing skills and encouraged me to transfer to Temple University and take journalism. Upon the recommendation of my instructor at Temple, I began to write for the student newspaper, which I consider one of my biggest achievements. Looking back, if Vicki and Linda had not suggested that I write the "On the Town" column for Compeer, I probably wouldn't have had the confidence to go back to college, let alone write for Community College or Temple University student newspapers.

Vicki asked me to speak on volunteerism at the 1995 International Compeer Conference in Philadelphia. I remember feeling that God gave me strength, and as I got further along in my speech, I began to realize that I was making a strong impact on the people who came to the workshop. I spoke about being empowered by helping my companion, Bob, in his recovery. When I finished my speech I got a standing ovation from the audience. Linda then came rushing up to the stage to give me a big hug. Kristen was also in the audience. She had come in that Friday afternoon from Washington, DC to see me give my presentation. It was simply one of the best days of my life.

My life became busier and I left Compeer to continue teaching and to pursue my studies at college. Then, one afternoon in 2002, while riding on the elevated train I saw a huge poster advertisement about Compeer. I saw that Compeer sign staring me in the face and I soon felt that God was letting me know that He wanted me to go back to the Compeer program. I believed it was God giving me a sign (no pun intended). In retrospect, I'm convinced that this is true. I decided to contact the Compeer office to try to become a volunteer again in the program where I had gained such confidence, increased my sensitivity, and began my development as a writer.

I was hesitant, however. Somewhere on my journey from one place to another, I had lost my identity. I had suffered a severe nervous breakdown and now lacked self-confidence. That emotional distress was compounded by my Tardive Dyskinesia.

I summoned up my courage and I made an appointment with Kathie, the program manager of Compeer in Philadelphia. I was touched that Kathie thought I would be a great asset for the program. I was also delighted to see my old friend, Ruby, from my earlier days as a volunteer. Kathie and Ruby treated me with kindness and respect, and I soon regained my identity.

She suggested that I write for the Compeer newsletter. However, this time I was writing on a variety of subjects, from covering a wellness and recovery workshop, to writing book reviews, to the benefits I have received from taking a tai chi class. Kathie also recommended me for state and national consumer conferences where I became inspired to become more involved in the consumer movement. I attended the state conference in Harrisburg last year and the Alternatives Conference in 2004, in Denver, on scholarships. Both conferences stressed that consumers should play an active role on committees and boards that affect mental health policy. Consequently, I joined the CSP (Community Support Program) committee in Philadelphia County, where Kathie and I co-chair the educational subcommittee. I have become more of an advocate and more open about my illness since returning to Compeer. I want to have an impact on consumers on a large scale and my work on the CSP committee gives me that opportunity.

When I came back to Compeer, I was matched with my companion, Steve. Steve was an acquaintance that I met several years ago at a singles function. When I went into the interview that Ruby set up for us, we were both pleasantly surprised that we were matched. Steve is very intelligent and enjoys going to a lot of activities that this fine city offers. We went to plays, restaurants, Phillies games, wrestling, movies, and visits with his mother. He started to become more comfortable in public as we went out regularly on Mondays. I feel privileged to help Steve and see him have a more active and enjoyable life.

Each October, Compeer has its annual banquet. I look forward to this special day as Compeer staff, volunteers, and their companions celebrate the program. This year, I went to the annual luncheon with Steve just expecting a nice outing. However, when Kathie started talking about the "Volunteer of the Year," I soon realized that she was talking about me! Kathie kept speaking of the different places I go with Steve, my writing for the newsletter, and how overall I contribute to the Compeer program. I was overwhelmed when Kathie said at the end of her talk that the "Volunteer of the Year" for 2004 is Jeff Shair! I was moved and honored to accept this award because I believe so much in the program.

My experience with Compeer has been very rewarding and gives me a sense of belonging. I have enjoyed going out with my companions and feel a great sense of pride as I watch them improve socially. My involvement with the program has made me more organized in my personal life. I feel thrilled that the Compeer staff have confidence in me to do tasks that I feel are challenging.

My confidence has improved significantly since I came back to the program, and I no longer see my Tardive Dyskinesia as an obstacle. I feel fortunate to have the opportunity to help others in their recovery. Since I became involved in the program, Compeer has given me a sense of purpose as the staff made me feel worthy of using me as a role model. I feel honored to be associated with this organization. Yes, I am aware of the extent I contributed to the Compeer Program, but what I have received cannot be measured.

I believe that my mother, father and brother, Paul, are smiling down on me from above and are proud of my success. The process of getting an opportunity where people have faith in me, and having that opportunity lead to even greater possibilities, is what I believe to be in God's Plan. Compeer has proven to be a wonderful experience where I have grown and flourished. Knowing this confirms my belief that I am in the place I was meant to be.

Reflections on Being a Compeer Volunteer

David Hoesly

Over the last two decades, I have been the Compeer friend to six teenagers: "Jack," "Steve," "Pete," "Cliff," "Chris," and "Sam." My pattern has been to take on a boy in his early-to-middle teen years and see him through when he turns eighteen or leaves high school, whichever happens later. Although I stay friends with the young men after they're launched into the world, my *weekly* commitment to them ends, and I take on another young man. My goals include the following:

1. to help my friend live up to his potential, however grand or limited that might be, so he becomes a head-healthy, self-reliant, productive member of society;
2   to help him see the beauty and joy in life, be it in nature or the arts or intellectual pursuits;

3. to teach him sensitivity, generosity, and the good feeling that comes from "doing the right thing" in life; and

4. to offer insights from lessons I've learned.

Benefits I personally receive include the satisfaction I get when I see the light bulb come on over their heads, when they "get" something I'm trying to teach them, whether it be how to paddle a canoe, ride a bike, play chess, troubleshoot an electrical circuit, factor an algebraic equation, etc. I most emphatically *do not* do this volunteering in any mushy-headed altruistic sense of "giving back" to the community, an idea that (as may be evident) I strongly reject.

In the twenty years with Compeer, I've had some sad experiences and many happy ones. Some of the former follow:

- visiting one friend in jail for repeated DWAI infractions;
- comforting a teary-eyed mom physically threatened by her son;
- providing "crash space" for one friend when he needed to flee his dysfunctional family; and
- learning of the murder of one friend by a drug dealer.

The happier events have outnumbered the sad ones, however, and they include these events:

- being the best man at one friend's wedding;
- watching one friend, age sixteen, finally master bicycle riding;
- helping one learn computer programming fundamentals (he's now a very successful system administrator);
- teaching one boy to wire a telephone extension for his bedroom;
- providing my refrigerator dolly, strong back, and weak mind to help several of them during their household moves; and
- exposing them to the joys of classical music and live theatrical performances.

In sum, being a Compeer volunteer has been, like most other life experiences, a mixed bag: many heartaches, but definitely more joys. I heartily endorse the program and its goals of providing friends to those with mental health problems. Not only can it be beneficial to the client *and* the volunteer, but also it's the right thing to do!

15. The Compeer Program and the Potential for Reducing Negative Attitudes toward Individuals with a Mental Illness

External Program Evaluation

Shannon M. Couture, M.A., David L. Penn, Ph.D., University of North Carolina at Chapel Hill

The Surgeon General of the United States has identified negative attitudes toward those with a mental illness as a significant roadblock to the treatment of mental disorders (US Department of Health and Human Services, 1999). Evidence suggests stigmatization of individuals with severe mental illnesses (SMI) may be one cause of the public's reluctance to allocate tax dollars for these individuals and may cause those with SMI to avoid seeking treatment. Indeed, many studies have shown that persons with SMI feel stigmatized by society (e.g., Wahl, 1999) and that the general public views persons with SMI negatively (e.g., Crisp et al., 2000). These negative attitudes include viewing persons with SMI as dangerous, unpredictable, and as being unlikely to get better (Crisp et al., 2000; Hayward and Bright, 1997). These stigmatizing attitudes are important because their existence results in a number of harmful consequences. Specifically, people with SMI are less likely to have apartments leased to them, less likely to be given job opportunities, and less likely to receive adequate health care (Lawrie, 1999; Link and Phelan, 2001). Thus, a concerted effort to support stigma-reducing campaigns and research is needed.

Researchers have argued one way to reduce the stigmatizing attitudes of the general public is to promote interpersonal contact between those with a mental illness and the general population. It is thought when contact occurs between a member of a stigmatized group (i.e., a person with SMI) and a member of the general population, people are likely to see the inaccuracy of some of their stereotypes and thus strive to change their attitudes toward the stigmatized group. Previous research has shown interpersonal contact to be effective at improving attitudes, but rarely have studies attempted to study contact as it would naturally occur, rather than as part of a forced, artificial laboratory situation (Couture & Penn, 2003). The Compeer program provides an excellent opportunity for the study of the effects of contact on attitudes in a naturalistic situation. We recruited volunteers from the Compeer program and compared them to volunteers from a similar agency working with individuals with developmental disabilities (the Association for Retarded Citizens (ARC) agency) and to individuals from the community who were not participating in any volunteer activity (Couture & Penn, in press).

All participants in the study were given questionnaires at two time points: before any volunteer activity occurred and six months after contact was initiated. We assessed participants attitudes about social distance (e.g., not wanting someone with a mental illness to move into one's neighborhood), perceived dangerousness of those with a mental illness, and emotional responses to those with SMI (e.g., rating whether one would be more likely to feel empathic or angry toward this group). We were interested in investigating whether negative attitudes toward this group as measured by these three scales would decrease over time for volunteers in the Compeer group. We expected the other two groups' attitudes to remain at the same level across time.

Our examination of the data revealed some promising findings. First, it appeared the Compeer volunteer group modestly improved their negative emotional responses toward those with SMI relative to individuals recruited from the community. In addition, it appeared that the strength of the relationship that was formed between the Compeer volunteers and their friends (i.e., how close the Compeer volunteer felt to their Compeer friend) was related to this decrease in negative emotional response toward SMI. These findings are important as it suggests contact can reduce negative attitudes toward mental illness and this effect can be observed through participating in a program like Compeer. Furthermore, this effect is promising given that the Compeer volunteers in our study had relatively positive attitudes at the initial assessment.

This study highlights another potential benefit of the Compeer program in addition to the other positive aspects associated with Compeer (such as providing much needed social support to those with SMI), namely the capacity to reduce stigma toward individuals with SMI. This effect may be more pronounced if the program could be offered to a wider array of individuals with varying degrees of stigmatizing attitudes.

References

Couture, S. M., & Penn, D. L. (2003). Interpersonal contact and the stigma of mental illness. *Journal of Mental Health* 12, 291–305.

Couture, S. M., & Penn, D. L. (in press). The effects of interpersonal contact on psychiatric stigma: A prospective approach utilitzing volunteers from the community. *Journal of Community Psychology.*

Crisp, A. H., Gelder, M. G., Rix, S., Meltzer, H. I., & Rowlands, O. J. (2000). Stigmatization of people with mental illnesses. *British Journal of Psychiatry,* 177, 4–7.

Hayward, P., & Bright, J. A. (1997). Stigma and mental illness: A review and a critique. *Journal of Mental Health,* 6, 345–54.

Lawrie, S. M. (1999). Stigmatization of psychiatric disorder. *Psychiatric Bulletin,* 23, 129–31.

Link, B. G., Phelan, J. C. (2001). Conceptualizing stigma. *Annual Review of Sociology,* 27, 363–85.

U.S. Department of Health and Human Services (1999). *Mental Health: A report of the Surgeon General.* Rockville, M.D.: U.S. Department of Health and Human Services, Substance Abuse and Mental Health Services Administration, Center for Mental Health Services, National Institute of Health, National Institute for Mental Health.

Wahl, O. F. (1999). Mental health consumers' experience of stigma. *Schizophrenia Bulletin,* 25, 467–78.

16. A Mixed Methods Study of the Benefits of Compeer Services

External Program Evaluation

Brian H. McCorkle, Ph.D., E. Sally Rogers, Sc.D., Erin C. Dunn, M.P.H., Yu Mui Wan, Ed.D., Asya Lyass, M.S., Ph.D. cand., Center for Psychiatric Rehabilitation, Boston University

In both professional and lay publications, people with serious mental illnesses have described a number of factors which they consider fundamental to their recovery process. However, many of these factors are not considered medically necessary by the medical community and therefore are not routinely offered by traditional mental health services. For example, even though they report that positive social experiences—such as social support from others or having someone who believes in them—promote recovery from mental illness (e.g., Deegan, 1990; Spaniol, Gagne, & Koehler, 1999), few opportunities exist for those experiences to occur.

For the general population, the beneficial effects of having social support are well documented in the research literature (e.g., Cohen, Mermelstein, Kanarck, & Hoberman, 1985; Schwazer & Leppin, 1989). Social support is viewed as a buffer against stressful life events (Cohen & Hoberman, 1983). However, many studies report that people with serious mental illness have smaller social networks than do people who do not have mental illness (Harris & Bergman, 1985; Baker, Jodrey, Intagliata, & Straus, 1993; Walsh & Connelly, 1996). People with psychiatric disabilities also report less satisfaction with their social support than either the general population or low-income individuals (Caron, Tempier, Mecier, & Leouffre, 1998). Inadequate social support also makes it more likely that people with psychiatric disabilities will experience an exacerbation of psychiatric symptoms (Leavy, 1983; Crotty & Kulys, 1985). Therefore, it appears that people with mental illness tend to have less social support than others, even though social support helps with mental illness.

Interventions have been developed for people with psychiatric disabilities both to increase the number of people in their social support networks (breadth) and to increase the amount of support received from those people (depth) (Harris & Bergman, 1985; Thornicroft & Breakley, 1991; McGrew, Bond, Dietzen, McKasson, et al., 1995). Many of the interventions described in this literature are non-traditional in that they involve support provided by non-professionals, either from community volunteers (Skirboll, 1994; Davidson et al., 2004) or from peers who are also mental health consumers (Mowbray & Tan, 1993; Perez, 1994; Chamberlin, Rogers, & Ellison, 1996; Wilson, Flanagan, & Rynders, 1999).

The Compeer program (Skirboll, 1994) matches community volunteers in one-to-one pairs with mental health consumers. These pairs agree to meet for at least one hour weekly or four hours monthly for at least one year, although some pairs continue for many years. Meetings included a wide range of social activities that friends might do together, such as meals or coffee, movies and plays, festivals and fairs, phone conversations, and the like. The purpose of the research described here was to evaluate the benefits of being in a Compeer pair for individuals with psychiatric disabilities. This project included both a quantitative (numeric and statistical) study of the outcomes of Compeer services and a qualitative (open-ended oral interview) study eliciting information about Compeer from its clients and volunteers in their own words.

Quantitative Study

Purpose. In order to observe what changes occurred as a result of Compeer services, our research team interviewed a group of mental health consumers several times during the course of their first year in a Compeer match. Mental health consumers on the Compeer waiting list were also interviewed during the same time period for comparison.

Research Methods. Because random assignment was not feasible in this fully operational services program in the community, a quasi-experimental research design (Campbell & Stanley, 1963) was developed. From 2001 until 2004, adult clients on the waiting lists of several Compeer offices in Upstate New York (Rochester, Elmira, and Utica) were invited to participate in the study at the time that they were matched with a Compeer volunteer. At the same time, another client on the waiting list was recruited for the comparison group. All participants in both groups were over 18 and were referred to Compeer by mental health providers as an adjunct to traditional mental health treatment. Therefore, all participants were receiving standard outpatient mental health services ("treatment as usual"); the only difference between groups was that the Matched group also met regularly with a Compeer volunteer.

The sample included seventy-nine clients in the Matched group (meeting with a Compeer volunteer) and seventy-five clients in the Waiting List comparison group. Participants were predominantly female (81%) and Caucasian (86%), with a wide range of age and marital status. Approximately 80% lived in independent housing, while most of the rest lived in group settings.

Data were gathered during face-to-face interviews at baseline, repeated at six and twelve months. Participants were reimbursed for each interview completed. *Social support* was assessed using the Interpersonal Support Evaluation List (or ISEL; Cohen & Hoberman, 1983). *Quality of Life, Social Inclusion* and *Social Acceptance* were assessed using the Lehman Brief Quality of Life Interview (Lehman, 1988) and the Well-Being Questionnaire (Campbell & Schraiber, 1989). *Self-esteem* was assessed using the Rosenberg Self-Esteem Scale (Rosenberg, 1965). *Empowerment* was assessed using the Empowerment Scale (Rogers, Chamberlin, Ellison, & Crean, 1997). *Psychiatric symptoms* were measured using the Hopkins Symptoms Checklist-25 (Mattsson, Williams, Rickels, Lipman, & Uhlenhuth, 1969) and the Colorado Symptom Index (Shern, Wilson, Coen, et al., 1994). *Relationship style,* a moderator variable, was measured using the Bartholomew scale (Bartholomew & Horowitz, 1991) to measure four attachment prototypes (secure, preoccupied, fearful, and dismissing).

Results. At baseline, there were no significant differences between the Matched group and the Waiting List group for any outcome measure, indicating that the two groups were similar at the beginning of the study. Analysis of Covariance (ANCOVA) was performed, controlling for baseline scores and relationship style. Mean scores for social support were significantly better for the Matched group than the Waiting List group at both six and twelve month assessments, indicating that participants perceived more social support than those in the Waiting List group during the course of the study. Participants in the Matched group also reported feeling a stronger sense of belongingness in terms of social support than the Waiting List participants at six and twelve months; this difference between groups was statistically significant at six months, but was only a strong trend at twelve months. Participants in the Matched group also reported receiving more assistance and having higher self-esteem than those in the Waiting List group at twelve months, as well as having a significantly higher sense of social inclusion. Not only did participants in the Matched group feel included, they also were more satisfied with the amount of friendship in their lives than the Waiting List participants. More fine-grained analyses of these data are nearing completion and will be submitted for publication in a peer-reviewed professional journal.

Qualitative Study

In order to develop a rich description of Compeer friendships, twenty people in matches were interviewed individually about their experience. Participants included both clients and volunteers, including one person who was both. One-third of the volunteers disclosed that they themselves were also mental health consumers. Participants were interviewed once for about one hour regarding the benefits and drawbacks of participating in the Compeer program, how Compeer services helped them and their match, how they had changed as a result of receiving or giving Compeer services, and whether they would recommend Compeer services to others in similar circumstances. Interviews were recorded with participants' knowledge and consent, and transcribed for qualitative analysis. Results, which are being prepared for publication in a professional peer-reviewed journal, highlighted the transformative power of meeting regularly with a friend who was neither a mental health professional nor a family member. Of particular interest, volunteers reported benefiting from this friendship themselves.

Summary

Results from both the quantitative and qualitative studies suggest that Compeer friendships have a significant, lasting, positive effect on social inclusion and social support, which are the two major areas which the Compeer program is designed to improve for mental health consumers. Consumers also developed higher self-esteem, more satisfaction with the friendships in their lives, and a greater sense of belongingness. In addition, volunteers reported the experience to be very rewarding and fulfilling. Data from both studies are in the final stages of analysis and will be submitted to appropriate peer-reviewed professional journals for publication.

References

Baker, F., Jodrey, D., Intagliata, J., & Straus, H. (1993). Community support services and functioning of the seriously mentally ill. *Community Mental Health Journal, 29*(4), 321–31.

Bartholomew, K., & Horowitz, L. M. (1991). Attachment styles among young adults: A test of a four-category model. *Journal of Personality and Social Psychology, 61*, 226–44.

Campbell, D., & Stanley, J. (1963). *Experimental and quasi-experimental designs for research.* Chicago: Rand-McNally.

Campbell, J., & Schraiber, R. (1989). *The Well-Being Project: Mental health consumers speak for themselves.* Sacramento, CA: California Dept. of Mental Health.

Caron, J., Tempier, R., Mercier, C., & Leouffre, P. (1998). Components of social support and quality of life in severely mentally ill, low income individuals and a general population group. *Community Mental Health Journal,* 34(5), 459–75.

Chamberlin, J., Rogers, E. S., & Ellison, M. L. (1996). Self-help programs: A description of their characteristics and their members. *Psychiatric Rehabilitation Journal,* 19(3), 33–42.

Cohen, S., & Hoberman, H. M. (1983). Positive events and social supports as buffers of life change stress. *Journal of Applied Social Psychology,* 13(2), 99–125.

Cohen, S., Mermelstein, R., Kamarck, T. E., & Hoberman, H. (1985). Measuring the functional components of social support. In I. G. Sarason & B. R. Sarason (Eds.), *Social support: Theory, research, and applications* (pp. 73–94). The Hague, The Netherlands: Martinus Nijhoff.

Crotty, P., & Kulys, R. (1985). Social support networks: The views of schizophrenic clients and their significant others. *Social Work,* 301–9.

Davidson, L., Shahar, G., Stayner, D. A., Chinman, M. J., Rakfeldt, J., & Tebes, J. K. (2004). Supported socialization for people with psychiatric disabilities: Lessons from a randomized controlled trial. *Journal of Community Psychology,* 32(4), 453–77.

Deegan, P. (1990). Spirit breaking: When the helping professions hurt. *Humanistic Psychologist,* 18(3), 301–13.

Harris, M., & Bergman, H. C. (1985). Networking with young adult chronic patients. *Psychosocial Rehabilitation Journal,* 8(3), 28–35.

Leavy, R. L. (1983). Social support and psychological disorder: A review. *Journal of Community Psychology,* 3–21.

Lehman, A. F. (1988). A quality of life interview for the chronically mentally ill. *Evaluation and Program Planning,* 11, 51–62.

Mattsson, N. B., Williams, H. V., Rickels, K., Lipman, E. H., & Uhlenhuth, E. H. (1969). Dimensions of symptom distress in anxious neurotic outpatients. *Psychopharmacology Bulletin,* 5, 19–32.

McGrew, J. H., Bond, G. R., Dietzen, L., McKasson, M., & et al. (1995). A multisite study of client outcomes in assertive community treatment. *Psychiatric Services,* 46(7), 696–701.

Mowbray, C. T., & Tan, C. (1993). Consumer-operated drop-in centers: Evaluation of operations and impact. *Journal of Mental Health Administration,* 20(1), 8–19.

Perez, C. (1994). Peer or mutual self-help in a Hispanic culture environment. In H. T. Harp & S. Zinman (Eds.), *Reaching across II: Maintaining our roots / The challenge of growth* (pp. 63–66). Sacramento, CA: California Network of Mental Health Clients.

Rogers, E. S., Chamberlin, J., Ellison, M. L., & Crean, T. (1997). A consumer-constructed scale to measure empowerment among users of mental health services. *Psychiatric Services,* 48(8), 1042–47.

Rosenberg, M. (1965). *Society and the adolescent self-image.* Princeton, NJ: Princeton University Press.

Schwarzer, R., & Leppin, A. (1989). Social support and health: A meta-analysis. *Psychology and Health,* 3(1), 1–15.

Shern, D. L., Wilson, N. Z., Coen, A. S., Patrick, D. C., & et al. (1994). Client outcomes: II. Longitudinal client data from the Colorado treatment outcome study. *Milbank Quarterly,* 72(1), 123–48.

Skirboll, B. (1994). The Compeer model: Client rehabilitation and economic benefits. *Psychosocial Rehabilitation Journal,* 18(2), 89–94.

Spaniol, L., Gagne, C., & Koehler, M. (1999). Recovery from serious mental illness: What it is and how to support people in their recovery. *Continuum,* 4(4), 3–15.

Thornicroft, G., & Breakey, W. R. (1991). The COSTAR Programme. 1: Improving social networks of the long-term mentally ill. *British Journal of Psychiatry,* 159, 245–49.

Walsh, J., & Connelly, P. R. (1996). Supportive behaviors in natural support networks of people with serious mental illness. *Health and Social Work,* 21(4), 296–303.

Wilson, M. E., Flanagan, S., & Rynders, C. (1999). The FRIENDS program: A peer support group model for individuals with a psychiatric disability. *Psychiatric Rehabilitation Journal,* 22(3), 239–47.

17. The Making of Friendships: Compeers Talk about Their Experiences in the Program

External Program Evaluation

Erin C. Dunn, M.P.H., Brian H. McCorkle, Ph.D., Yu Mui Wan, Ed.D., and Cheryl Gagne, Sc.D., Center for Psychiatric Rehabilitation, Boston University

What does the match process look like from the point of view of Compeer clients and volunteers? What actually happens when clients and volunteers are matched in the Compeer program? And what do these program participants think about Compeer activities, money, decision-making, and other related topics?

Researchers from Boston University conducted several research studies of Compeer Services between 2001 and 2004. The effectiveness of Compeer as a service is described briefly in Chapter 16 and will be published in more detail in professional journals. The purpose of this chapter is to describe the perspective of clients and volunteers with respect to their participation in the program. This chapter is separated into the following sections: (1) Getting Started with the Compeer Program, (2) What the Matches Do Together, (3) Negotiating the Friendship, (4) Involvement with the Local Compeer Office, and (5) Other Issues Worth Highlighting.

To gather data for this particular part of the project, we interviewed a total of twenty clients and volunteers who were all affiliated with the Compeer program in Rochester, New York. Participants were balanced between three groups based on length of match: less than one year, between one and two years, and more than three years. Interviews lasted about one hour and covered a variety of aspects of people's experience in the Compeer program. More detailed information about the people that were interviewed and the procedures involved in conducting these interviews can be found in forthcoming articles.

I. Getting Started in the Compeer Program

Reasons for Joining Compeer

Clients typically heard about the Compeer program from mental health professionals, family members, or advertising. They described a number of reasons for joining the Compeer program. All clients joined the Compeer program because they wanted to have a friend, as many describe having few friends. They talked about the desire to get out of the house, participate in social activities, and have someone to talk to. The Compeer program was seen by many as providing the opportunity to meet people and for one participant, to learn something about life. However, one participant described mixed feelings about joining the program, which she likened to a woman using an escort service for a companion to attend the opera.

For some clients, the desire to have a Compeer friend went beyond having someone to take them out of the house and also included someone with whom the person could both provide and receive support. These individuals described the desire to both *have* a friend and *be* a friend. One participant described this sentiment by saying:

> "So I thought it'd be a way to get to know somebody, hopefully, and they'd get to know me and . . . there'd be a part of somebody who's caring about me, even though they didn't know me too well, but then they would get to know me and just become a friend . . . we do have our, we do keep our distance of sorts. But if something was necessary, I needed something, and he needed to do something, it could be done."

Another person described the wish to have a non-professional involved in making the adjustment from institutional to community living who is not "gonna analyze every single word I say . . . that's gonna help me from being locked up in the state hospital, to living on my own, and having hope."

Volunteers described the desire to give back to the community and contribute to others as one major reason why they joined the Compeer program. Volunteers who were not consumers sometimes also mentioned wanting to learn more about mental illness in order to help someone who has these experiences. They also described the feeling of empathy and the conviction that everyone needs a friend. One volunteer commented, "How would you like it if you had no friends?" For volunteers who are also mental health consumers, this feeling was often based on their own personal experience, either because they had gone through periods, such as hospitalizations with no social supports, or because they had received support from family during those times but knew fellow consumers who had struggled alone.

Personal experience also prompted some of the non-consumer volunteers to participate. For example, volunteers described how they witnessed the loneliness and isolation of their family members with mental illness. One person saw the benefit of the Compeer program first-hand when a family member was involved in the program.

Volunteers also described several other pathways to joining Compeer. Several mentioned being prompted to participate by advertising or other external agents. One participant was persuaded by a co-worker who was a long time member of Compeer and another described how his company was promoting the program. Another stated that he saw there was a need and "answered that plea."

Many volunteers were already interested in volunteering and found that Compeer was a good outlet for this interest, both because of the one-to-one interaction (as opposed to serving on a board) and because the time expectation was so reasonable. Others described wanting to do something stimulating in their free time and find different experiences in life. One retired mental health professional wanted to stay connected to the field. For several people, retirement or bereavement opened up time for volunteering and Compeer's one-to-one model replaced some of the daily social interactions with family or colleagues that was missing.

The Match Process: Client's Perspective

Clients reported spending between six months and two years on the waiting list before being matched, which many found frustrating. Some also disliked the amount of paperwork required as part of the match, but others remarked on how well the Compeer staff matched clients and volunteers. Participants attributed this to matching based on similar interests and backgrounds or because Compeer staff thought that "opposites attract."

The Match Process: Volunteer's Perspective

Volunteers described a variety of characteristics that were important in the match process. Attention was paid to matching clients and volunteers based on some personal characteristic such as age, housing location, and shared interests. Most volunteers chose either adult or child/adolescent clients, although some volunteers reported being willing to work with either age level. Volunteers thought that Compeer generally tried to match them with clients who live in the same area. The client's proximity to the volunteer's home was something that was considered to be important for the volunteer. In addition to these preferences, volunteers also described how they wanted to be matched with someone who owned a car or had similar hobbies or interests. The client's psychiatric illness was occasionally considered relative to the volunteer's experience and comfort with mental illness.

Meeting the Match and Starting a Friendship

Initial meetings between the client and volunteer often occurred in a public setting (e.g. restaurant, coffee shop), although it was up to the volunteer to initiate contact to figure out what the client was comfortable doing. There was a wide range of experiences with this first meeting. While some reported "hitting if off immediately," others describe how the connection evolved very slowly. Both clients and their volunteers sometimes described feeling nervous to meet one another.

II. What the Matches Do Together

Description of Activities

Volunteers and clients were consistent in reporting a wide range of activities. Each of these activities varied in terms of expense. Activities occurred in public, private, and community settings.

The most frequently mentioned activity was to meet to talk over coffee or a meal. Another common activity focused around entertainment such as movies (with or without a meal or dessert), theatrical productions, and sporting events. The range in expense of these activities is illustrated by theatrical productions that included school productions, community theatre, regional professional theater, and touring Broadway productions. Many pairs also planned special outings to destinations such as museums, art galleries, fairs, festivals, boat trips on the local canal, and viewing Christmas lights by car. Some made arrangements for physical activities such as miniature golf, skiing, swimming at the Y, power walking, and bowling. Some pairs also engaged in more private activities, such as Thanksgiving and Christmas activities, dinner at home, watching videos, and family get-togethers. These events, if they occurred, were more likely to be at the volunteer's home than the client's home. Several matches included community events among their activities. These included making holiday decorations for Meals on Wheels, visiting sick children at the holidays, Christmas caroling, and volunteer organizations. In extremely unusual cases, one person visited a religious meeting frequented by the other person, and one pair (in which the volunteer also had a history of mental illness) sometimes attended self-help groups together. Once pairs were well established, some enjoyed just getting together: talking by phone, visiting bookstores, talking walks, window shopping, or engaging in arts and crafts together.

Some volunteers assisted their Compeer friend in practical ways, such as driving them for grocery shopping or to run errands that were easier by car than bus. One volunteer helped his friend with money management, teaching him how to develop a budget and get out of credit card debt. Other volunteers helped their friends to redecorate, build storage, and so on.

Duration and Frequency of Activities

The overall length of time spent meeting together and the frequency with which matches met followed several patterns. About one-third of the participants reported meeting weekly at the same day and time, usually for an hour to an hour-and-a-half. As one volunteer said, "They ask you to spend about an hour a week with the person, and that's perfect because I can always, you know, fit an hour in the week." Some pairs had to modify that arrangement occasionally to accommodate the client's or volunteer's work schedule. Several pairs also spent time talking on the phone, typically on a weekly basis.

Pairs that met in the evening were much more likely to spend several hours at a time, often because of longer activities such as movies. Sometimes pairs that meet during the day for lunch also spent an extra hour or two shopping. Pairs that did not have regular times generally met between two and four times a month for several hours each time. A small minority of Compeer friendships were more informal and unstructured: "It's hard to say. It comes, it goes in spurts. Just like a friend—you don't say an hour a week."

Factors Affecting Activities

Both clients and volunteers reported a number of factors that affected the activities they did together. Although some factors affected primarily either the client or volunteer, many factors affected both equally. The factors reported by the participants appear to cluster together in the three separate categories: (1) time constraints, (2) physical (pragmatic) factors, and (3) psychological factors.

Time Constraints

Employment. The first set of time constraints revolved around employment. Most volunteers and several clients reported that their work schedule limited the times available to meet. One client reported that they met "pretty much once a week, except at the time I was working crazy hours sometimes, and that sometimes interfered with our ability to meet." Volunteering during retirement potentially reduced this constraint, although some retirees were so busy with other activities that scheduling remained an issue, causing one client to report feeling "penciled in" on her retired volunteer's schedule. However, neither clients nor volunteers reported that scheduling around work was an undue burden. One volunteer commented that lunch works well for those with jobs or other time demands because "for a busy person, that works out because you're going to have the lunch anyhow."

Family. Many clients and volunteers noted that family obligations limited the time available for either the client or volunteer. One volunteer said, "I would like it if we *could* meet more often. But sometimes, due to our schedules–hers and mine, her time with her mother, my time with my family–that hinders that." Some participants mentioned taking care of children or grandchildren as well as aging parents. Other obligations mentioned included family birthdays, holidays, and similar events, as well as being out of town to visit family or take a vacation.

Time of Day/Week. The time of day or day of week available to meet was also a factor participants described as affecting activities. Some matches deliberately avoided meeting in the evening or on weekends in order not to intrude on time with the client's or volunteer's family. Other matches organized their meeting time around whether the client or volunteer was considered a "morning" or "evening" person. In addition to this ordinary variation among people, many psychiatric medications can cause early morning drowsiness and some clients reported not being able to leave the house until mid-morning.

Flexibility. A final consideration was flexibility about time. When both the client and volunteer could be flexible about meeting time and day, participants reported being able to accommodate irregular occurrences such as illness, appointments, and the like. However, some matches reported that a regular, fairly invariable schedule made it easier to meet regularly. In addition, although Compeer requests a commitment of one hour weekly, certain activities (such as movies and shows, or driving to museums and festivals at a distance) can only occur if both the Compeer friends are able to devote more time to the activity. Therefore, matches that met weekly for coffee or lunch were less likely to report variation in what they did together.

Physical (Pragmatic) Factors

Transportation and Distance. The physical location of activities and the available modes of transportation for both the client and volunteer affected the feasibility of certain activities. Most (but not all) volunteers had cars. Conversely, most (but not all) clients did not have cars. For some matches, therefore, the location and frequency of bus routes played a large role in determining activities. Even when cars were available, certain interesting activities were located farther away than client or volunteer could travel, either due to time available or physical discomfort.

Weather. A factor that frequently and often unexpectedly affects activities in Western Upstate New York is weather, especially snow. Sometimes this takes the form of canceling activities, but one pair reported having planned a ski outing, which had to be cancelled due to insufficient snow. A second way that weather affected activities is that Rochester is one of the cloudier cities in North America and some volunteers reported that dreary days increased the likelihood that their client match would not feel up to a planned activity.

Money. Finances played a significant role for many pairs. Compeer's expectation, in theory, is that clients are to pay their own way. Given the income disparity between most volunteers and clients, many volunteers found creative ways to circumvent this rule or even ignore it outright, as discussed in the section below. Nevertheless, finances ruled out expensive activities such as upscale restaurants or high cost entertainment. Many volunteers would actively search for coupons, special days with free admission, two-for-one deals, and the like in order to accommodate the client's income without shaming the client by paying his or her way. The local Compeer office assisted these efforts by procuring coupons and publicizing deals in the monthly newsletter, which both clients and volunteers reported to appreciate.

Physical Health. The physical health of either the client or volunteer was often mentioned as ruling out or at least limiting participation in certain activities. In addition to strenuous activities such as hikes, sometimes even walking around a festival was too physically demanding, especially if one or both people had a physical disability or were overweight. Such constraints were frequently mentioned by elderly Compeer friends. These physical health problems were reported to interfere with activities either directly through limiting strength, stamina, and flexibility, or indirectly by increasing the frequency of medical treatment with its associated time and expense.

Psychological Factors

Preferences and Interests. The most obvious psychological factor is what the client and volunteer are each interested in doing. As one person said, "If he doesn't like something, then we won't do it together. We have to jointly agree on the one thing . . If we don't agree on a certain thing, then, together we agree on something else . . . ." Both clients and volunteers said they were likely to suggest activities that either they were personally interested in or that they thought the other person would be interested in. The section below on decision-making describes these occurrences in greater detail.

Flexibility. Both clients and volunteers reported trying new things that they were introduced to by the other person in the match. Some clients and volunteers, however, were less willing to try new things. This oftentimes resulted in frustration for the other person. The ways in which Compeer friends negotiated this is described below.

Client Motivation. Some volunteers reported that client motivation was a strong determinant of what they did. For example, a few volunteers reported that their Compeer friend were sometimes not motivated to try new things, or even to do anything at times. Other volunteers said their Compeer friend was not motivated to do things to improve their physical health (such as walking or swimming). However, such statements imply that the volunteers had decided for themselves that their friend "should" engage in such activities and therefore there was a value on the part of the volunteers that their friend did not share.

Client Mood. A small group of clients appeared to be strongly affected by their mood state. In particular, some clients (and their volunteers) reported that they were less likely to engage when depressed. For example, "there are some days she can't kind of psych herself up to do that" [get on a bus to meet the volunteer]. In addition to energy and motivation, sometimes this affected client self-confidence to try new activities. This suggests that volunteers working with clients with a history of depression would benefit from training about dealing with this specific issue. Also, it suggests that matches begun when clients are depressed may be less likely to work out than matches begun when not depressed.

Commitment. Successful matches require commitment by clients as well as volunteers, including a commitment to meet even when they would rather not. This might take the form of meeting even when feeling reticent or tired. Without this commitment on the part of either the client or volunteer, the relationship does not work for the volunteer, leading to frustration and possibly the end of the match.

III. Negotiating the Friendship

Making Decisions

There were three general patterns of scheduling meetings. First, many pairs decided during one meeting when the next meeting would be. A second pattern involved meeting routinely on the same day and time every week or two, often for a meal or coffee. Third, some pairs had less regular, more spontaneous meetings, frequently initiated by either member of the pair calling the other to invite them to something specific. Many pairs showed some flexibility, combining some routine with occasional spontaneous events. Similarly, some pairs spoke by phone between meetings, either to cancel meetings or have a conversation when the client needed to talk to someone. The approach used seems to result from a combination of schedules, preferences, and personality styles of both the client and volunteer.

The majority of participants jointly decided what activities they would do with their match, describing mutual and shared decision-making, which consisted of "give and take." This might involve taking turns, although more often one person in the pair tended to generate more and present them to the other. In some matches, however, decisions about activities were clearly dictated by either the client or volunteer. In rare cases the client's range of preferred activities was extremely narrow (such as only going to the same restaurant or coffee shop), which some, though not all, volunteers found frustrating. In other cases the client always deferred to the volunteer. Some volunteers reported that the constant generation of ideas for activities was burdensome.

Some participants reported struggles around making decisions. In some cases this reflected strong personality styles of either the client or volunteer. In other cases one person had a very strong interest in an activity that the other disliked. Volunteers reported receiving support from Compeer staff in dealing with such difficulties, but one client mentioned struggling with these issues without the same kind of support.

Money

Nearly all volunteers mentioned that their friend had a limited amount of money, and therefore activities were selected accordingly. The general expectation from Compeer is that expenses will be split evenly between volunteer and client, but there is considerable variation among client-volunteer pairs. Many (if not most) volunteers contribute more than half the expense. In many cases this was because two-for-one coupons for meals or ticket (often donated to Compeer) were used; volunteers would usually pay their own way and use the coupons to cover the clients' expense. Some pairs scrupulously split everything equally. More rarely, volunteers appeared to contribute more and may even provide small amounts of spending money, cigarettes, and the like to client, though this seemed to primarily involve clients who were in the hospital rather than living in the community.

The difference in financial means is a potential source of tension in the relationship. A few clients expected their volunteers to pay for more than half or even to buy things for them due to being better off financially, which some volunteers resented. In other cases the volunteers expected to pay more or even prevent their friend from paying at all, which their friend could experience as condescending or shaming (although no one stated this explicitly). However, there were other cases in which everything was split evenly without discord and still other cases in which the volunteer provided extra in a way that is satisfactory to both. Similarly, in some pairs both client and volunteer gave presents (holidays, birthday, etc.) to each other, while in some pairs presents were primarily from volunteer to client and in other pairs no gifts were exchanged.

Interestingly, volunteers who were themselves consumers were especially sensitive to the dynamics around money but tended towards the extremes, either always paying for the client (to acknowledge the clients' limited income) or never paying for the client (to "normalize" the relationship and make it as mutual as possible). One consumer-volunteer went as far as saying "it sabotages the relationship for the volunteer to always pay." This highlights that no two relationships are exactly the same, but are complex interactions of the client and volunteer. It seems important that pairs start with the Compeer guidelines of equal shares and then engage in explicit verbal negotiations about any variations from these guidelines. In fact, this negotiation process is part of the experience of a healthy relationship with a friend, and therefore one way that Compeer is of benefit.

IV. Involvement with the Local Compeer Office

Participation in Compeer Activities

The Compeer office in Rochester offers a variety of activities beyond the formal Compeer matches. Some are sporadic, including holiday parties, summer picnics, and special excursions such as museum trips, movies, or sporting events. Others are ongoing programs often designed to provide some support for clients on the waiting list.

Both clients and volunteers reported varying degrees of interest with respect to participating in Compeer activities. The majority of people reported being interested in and having enjoyed participating in at least some Compeer activities, but there was tremendous variability. Some matches rarely missed a Compeer activity, while other matches had no interest in them at all. Sometimes volunteers and clients reported different interest levels in this regard: when volunteers wanted to participate and clients did not, some clients reported feeling pressured. However, the majority of both clients and volunteers said they wanted to see more opportunities for people to get together.

Both clients and volunteers reported experiencing a number of benefits as a result of their participation in Compeer Activities. For example, many reported that these activities were beneficial because they did not require a lot of money (such as when a ski trip was donated or paid for by Compeer).

Others thought that these structured activities were better than informal meetings in that they provided a break from "the usual ice cream or dinner out." Many clients reported that these activities gave them the chance to socialize, which they reported to not have the opportunity to do very often. Volunteers thought that clients really enjoyed the attention that was focused on them during these activities. Volunteers also discussed how the Compeer Conflict Group gave them the opportunity to learn tips on how to interact with their match.

On the other hand, a few clients mentioned drawbacks related to participating in Compeer activities. One client discussed the stigma or shame associated with being a participant in any Compeer-related function. Another person reported not liking to participate in a Compeer activity because it seemed demeaning to the participants. Two clients felt uncomfortable participating in these activities because they did not feel like they fit in.

Interactions with the Local Compeer Office Staff

Volunteers described how Compeer staff members were available when needed to provide suggestions, be supportive in difficult situations around Compeer guidelines, and assist in ending difficult matches that were not improving. Volunteers reported feeling supported through these interactions with staff and also benefited from networking with other volunteers. Although a few clients and volunteers found Compeer's guidelines regarding boundaries between clients and volunteers more restrictive than they liked, most participants appear to have found such guidelines helpful.

Volunteers, including consumer-volunteers, who reported extensive interaction with the local Compeer office mentioned participating in board meetings, assisting in mailings, collecting prizes for various activities, and assisting in recruiting other volunteers. Those with the highest organizational participation tended to be either new or experienced volunteers with unusually high levels of commitment to Compeer. It appears that volunteer participation in the organizational side of Compeer may tend to decrease after the initial flush of enthusiasm.

Client interactions with the Compeer organization appear to be more limited in scope, such that the only interaction many clients had with the organization occurred when they were invited to participate in specific programs (e.g., quilt-making) or events (e.g., picnics). Some clients attend these programs or events rarely because they felt these events were geared towards people who are "low-functioning." It appears that the major way for "higher functioning" clients to increase interaction with Compeer is to become volunteers or board members, which is described in greater detail in the section below.

V. Other Issues Worth Highlighting

Reason Previous Matches Ended

Close to half of the clients and volunteers we met with described having had at least one previous match. The reasons why these matches ended varied considerably and included moving (i.e. client moved far away from the volunteer), poor chemistry between the client and volunteer, lack of commitment on the part of the volunteer, the client not being stable enough for a match, and the client ending their treatment with a therapist (a requirement of the program). Two volunteers said that previous matches ended because the client died of physical health causes. In some rare cases, the relationship ended as a result of conflict. Several clients and consumer volunteers reported that the ending of the previous match was a difficult one. Some suggested that Compeer should conduct exit interviews with each individual in order to explore the reasons for the match coming to a close. Some of the matches ended because the client "outgrew" the need for a volunteer and some of the clients we met with went on to become volunteers.

Consumers as Compeer Volunteers

Differences From Non-Consumers Volunteers

One of our research questions centered around whether volunteers who were themselves consumers of mental health services differed from individuals who were not consumers with respect to their relationship with their Compeer friend and participation in the program. It appears that being a consumer-volunteer does in fact make a difference, though there were some volunteers and clients who said they did not think that being a consumer mattered. The ways in which being a consumer were thought to make a difference are discussed below.

Very generally, being a consumer-volunteer sometimes meant that the volunteer went the extra mile to connect with his or her friend, such as visiting the client while he/she was in the hospital. It also may have meant staying in Compeer after having a match come to a close. For one consumer-volunteer, having a history of mental illness contributed both to her getting into the Compeer program and staying with the program after a first match ended. Volunteers who were also consumers thought that they may need more support than volunteers without mental illness. This may include encouragement in terms of setting limits, especially when they first start the match.

Having a personal history with mental illness was something that several consumer-volunteers believed helped them to have a better understanding of clients. They reported having a better understanding of what the client was going through. Volunteers said they knew exactly how their friend felt and were able to relate to the person's problems, even though their own were sometimes long ago. The sentiment of "been there, done that" was expressed repeatedly. For one consumer-volunteer, volunteers who were consumers had a greater tolerance, compassion, and patience for their friend based on their own understanding of the illness or disability. For all of these reasons, consumer-volunteers were very happy to know that so many volunteers were consumers, though one person felt that consumers were underutilized as volunteers.

Clients and consumer-volunteers also talked about how volunteers who were also consumers had the potential to become role models to the clients by demonstrating that recovery was possible. According to one consumer-volunteer, it can be helpful to the client to have a volunteer who has also experienced mental problems in the past and other life hardships, but who now has a good job and relationships and who seems so "normal." However, this situation was also at times a difficult one for this particular match, especially when the friend would compare herself to the volunteer in a self-deprecating way (e.g. idea of why can't I overcome my problems and be like you). This situation also raises questions about the degree to which volunteers who are also consumers discuss their own personal experience with mental illness and psychiatric treatment, which will be discussed in a forthcoming article.

Transition from Client to Volunteer

Consumer-volunteers described the transition from being a client to becoming a volunteer. One person described it as a "natural evolution" and another described having "graduated" from a client to a volunteer (and board member). This particular person thought that this transition was the way the Compeer program should work.

A few clients thought about becoming volunteers in the future, though nearly all of these clients believed they were unsuitable due to a lack of having money or a car. There were also several clients who discussed issues related to being ready to transition into a volunteer role. For example, one client wanted to improve his social skills, feel more comfortable in social groups, and figure out how to balance work and a volunteering commitment before becoming a volunteer. There was also the idea of being ready to give more of yourself, which one client described as moving from "me, me, me to them, them, them." Some clients also talked about how their volunteers encouraged them to start volunteering.

What Makes a Good Volunteer

Volunteers described a number of qualities they thought were necessary for someone to be considered a good volunteer. These included being a good listener, a compassionate person, and willing to share with someone who was less fortunate. Volunteers also thought a good volunteer was someone who did not give their friend too much advice and who could listen to their friend without telling them how to solve their problem or try to fix it for them. It also meant not talking too much about yourself and sharing "how good you have it." Volunteers also talked about the importance of treating the client like a friend and not an obligation, by not making the client feel as though the volunteer was really volunteering, even though both people know this is the case. One volunteer said a good volunteer was someone who was genuine about it; a person who would become a Compeer volunteer for the purpose of adding it to his or her resume was not someone who was thought of as a good volunteer. From the point of view of the client, someone with a mental health background (e.g. training or being a former counselor) was considered to be a good volunteer.

Recruiting Volunteers

Volunteers also discussed their own participation in these formal recruitment efforts. Although clients and volunteers both unanimously said they would recommend the program to others, the degree to which participants actually tried to recruit volunteers varied considerably. While many volunteers attempted to actively recruit individuals to become volunteers, others did not. These individuals talked about the program favorably to others, but would not aggressively try to get other people to volunteer. Some volunteers said they would recommend the Compeer program to their friends if they thought they would actually join. Many volunteers expressed how their effort to recruit volunteers was oftentimes unsuccessful, though there were some exceptions.

Overall, there was a general sense of not understanding why other people would not want to volunteer for the Compeer program. Volunteers discussed their frustration around trying to recruit other volunteers to the extent that one volunteer described it as rejection. Several volunteers discussed the reasons people often provided for not volunteering, such as not having enough time, wanting to wait until they had less responsibility, or being selfish, all of which were thought to be poor excuses. For example, one volunteer said, "I just don't understand why it's quite such a hard sell. I think people just imagine that the responsibility is far more immense that it is . . . it's play. That I think they see it as someone bigger and heavier than it is." Many volunteers and some clients also described how empathy towards a person in need should be one reason why people choose to volunteer.

Although the majority of volunteers expressed a lack of understanding about why people were hesitant to join the program, many talked about stigma or negative attitudes towards people with mental illness as a barrier to recruiting volunteers. For example, one volunteer said, "People have trouble with mental illness. They're afraid of it, they don't understand it," and another said, "People hear the word 'mental illness' and they get scared." These negative attitudes and images related to mental illness are discussed in greater detail in the next section.

Stigma

Participants described several stereotypes or negative attitudes towards people with mental illness, including the belief that all people with mental health issues are extremely low functioning, incompetent, violent, and have nothing to offer society. Volunteers reported that the media and where one grew up shaped these attitudes. For example, one volunteer who had very negative attitudes towards people with mental illness prior to starting the program said, "I grew up in the area when there weren't mental hospitals, they were insane asylums, and people weren't mentally ill, they were crazy." On the contrary, another volunteer described how her generally positive attitude towards all people with disabilities was based on her exposure to people with physical disabilities while growing-up. Nearly every participant discussed how these negative attitudes contributed to people being afraid. One client, who was transitioning from the state hospital into the community, described the challenge to integrate into her community because "the whole world sees this great big badge on my shoulder saying 'I'm nuts.'" For this reason, this particular client was happy to be entering a relationship where the other person already knew she had a mental illness.

Stigma influenced the reaction volunteers received from their friends and family as a result of participating in Compeer. One volunteer described how former friends questioned why she wanted to have a friend "like that," while a consumer-volunteer described receiving a warm reception from his friends after introducing them to his Compeer friend. Experience and exposure to people with mental illness were seen as one way of changing these negative attitudes. In this regard, several volunteers discussed how participation in the Compeer program was a way of reducing or outgrowing stigma.

Also worth noting was the degree to which clients wanted to be "open" about their participation in Compeer. On the one hand, being seen participating in Compeer activities was reported to have been embarrassing to clients and their families. On the other hand, one client wanted to be very public about her involvement and experience with Compeer because "it would give people an understanding that mental health doesn't mean the psychotic, murderous person." These differences illustrate that not every client is comfortable about being "out of the closet" with respect to their psychiatric disability.

Conclusion

The information summarized in this chapter highlights the core components of the Compeer friends program, as articulated by the program's participants. We reviewed the processes involved in getting connected to the Compeer program and the initial stages of the match process. We also discussed the activities friends do together and the ways in which they navigate their friendship, including how they handle difficult situations. Involvement with the local Compeer office and participation in Compeer activities was also discussed. We concluded this chapter by reviewing other relevant information, such as consumers as Compeer volunteers, the characteristics of a good volunteer, recruiting volunteers, and stigma or negative attitudes towards people with mental illness. This information is intended to supplement the work that we did in evaluating the overall effectiveness of the program, which is reviewed in Chapter 16 and will be published in forthcoming articles.

18. Projections for the Future

Bernice W. Skirboll, M.S.

Over thirty years ago, Compeer was a tiny program launched from my desk at the Rochester Psychiatric Center, and now it is a flourishing program on two continents. We have discussed Compeer's impact on the lives of its participants and its professionals, and its effect on the mental health system and on the rest of society. In this chapter, we look toward the future and share some of the issues that will challenge Compeer. These include resource development, recruitment of volunteers, the stigma of mental illness, and the obstacles to growth of a grassroots organization. I will discuss the steps Compeer is taking to meet these challenges.

Resource Development

Compeer strives to offer high quality programs in response to each community's needs. We face the major challenge of obtaining enough financial resources to enable us to provide these programs. Financial concerns affect us whether we are starting a Compeer program in a new community, or building, enhancing, and growing an existing program.

Most nonprofit organizations rely in part on the charity of the individuals they serve and on the families of those individuals. Unlike some of the mentally ill, sufferers of other types of illness are sometimes in a financial position to make generous contributions. Upon release from the hospital after having received successful treatment, some patients are so pleased with their outcome that they donate money to the hospital, to research efforts, or to service organizations. Compeer faces the challenge of serving a population that lacks discretionary spending money. Mental illness inhibits a large percentage of its sufferers from achieving gainful employment. At Compeer when we build our donor system, we cannot depend upon the individuals we serve as a base of donors. And in many cases, due to the lack of support from the mental health system, the families of our clients become impoverished while caring for their loved ones, and are unable to lend financial support to Compeer.

At Compeer, we have learned to deal innovatively with financial challenges by discovering unmet needs in the community, and by developing new programs to meet these needs. The creation of new programs leads to new funding opportunities and sources. We must continuously be creative enough to identify the problems in the community and to determine what needs to be accomplished. An example of this is the Juvenile Drug Court Mentoring Program in Rochester, New York. When a family court judge established this program, he believed that there was one missing piece that was desperately needed to augment the services provided by the program. The missing piece was a way to provide positive role models from the community to guide the youths. Compeer responded to this need, secured the necessary funding, and supplied mentors and more through our Juvenile Drug Court Mentoring program.

One message we learned was that when you start a project, you have to know when to cut your losses. For example, we thought that the homeless population was a perfect group to receive Compeer's services. Many of the homeless suffered from mental illness. But, we soon discovered that their situation did not fit the Compeer model. Generally speaking, homeless people were on the move and had no consistent address. Compeer could not serve their needs because we could not keep track of where they were. It is true that one's goals should always be to serve a specific population in whichever way you can and not be married to one approach. That has been Compeer's way since the beginning. But, in this case, we had to realize that there was nothing Compeer could do to help this population.

Sometimes creativity demands that we shift gears on a moment's notice. Recently, several Compeer staff members and I made a presentation to a foundation that has supported us for years. At the end of the presentation we were told that the foundation had recently changed its priorities and in the future will only fund programs designed to help the developmentally disabled. They regretted that they could no longer finance Compeer. I had to think fast. I remembered that many of our clients suffer from developmental disabilities in additional to their mental illness, although this was not widely publicized. After I explained this to the donor foundation, they were more than happy to continue to support us.

Funds are also available to the programs that can tap into the current goals of the mental health system. One such goal is consumer empowerment. We feel the greatest excitement and pride when one of our clients "graduates" to become a Compeer volunteer. This is a form of consumer empowerment. We can develop programs that utilize consumers' skills, and then apply for grants to fund these programs.

To run a successful Compeer program, we must keep our knowledge about the mental health system current. We must be in the forefront of change and be visible in the community we serve. By being involved and well informed and by being a key player at the table, we learn about funding opportunities. Look at Compeer's history. When we went from serving patients in the state hospital through "Adopt-A-Patient," to serving the newly de-institutionalized individuals through Compeer, we were responding creatively to the changing mental health system, as well as the needs of the people in the community. In turn, new funding sources became available to us. If Compeer had remained a hospital-based program, we would not have created the rich variety of services we now offer, and we would not be the internationally recognized model mental health program that we are today. Challenges demand creativity. Creativity results in more appropriate programs, better outcomes, and more people served. One of Compeer's greatest strengths is the ability to be flexible and to modify the model to serve people who are multiply disabled. Multiple disabilities may include mental illness, physical illness, congenital problems, as well as developmental disabilities and substance abuse. Think about the value of a Compeer to someone who not only has one disability, but multiple disabilities. When we create new programs to serve the multiplied disabled, we meet an unmet need, and we become eligible for new funding opportunities from fresh streams of funding.

Another creative approach is to identify groups of people who are struggling with mental illness, who are not receiving adequate services. We are pursing a new initiative in Rochester, New York, the veterans outreach program called "Compeer Volunteers for Vets." The wars of the past decade have led to a surge in the number of returning veterans. Many veterans have mental health issues. We saw this as a challenge, so we acted creatively and came up with the idea of matching the suffering veterans with others who have also experienced war, but who have not been traumatized by it. Organizers of this new program plan to tap into the resources of the Veterans Administration system for funding.

Another service new to Compeer is the Mentoring Children of Prisoners program, which started in 2004. This one-to-one program specifically serves youth with an incarcerated parent. Compeer is collaborating with Catholic Family Center for this service.

Sometimes a program takes on a life of its own, such as our Skillbuilders' Quilting Bee program. Many of the women in the Quilting Bee are dually diagnosed from residential or transitional placements. In fact, because of the successful outcomes for some of these women, one of our community referral sources has made our quilting group part of their curriculum of group therapy.

This project has come up with an innovative approach to obtaining financial resources. In order to help with expenses, the Compeer Quilting Bee holds a quilt sale twice a year and does some consignment quilts. The women are learning some business skills: pricing quilts by the time and cost of fabrics, inventory, budgeting, and marketing.

One of women in the program had this to say about her experience in the Compeer Quilting Bee:

I have been diagnosed with clinical depression, anxiety attacks and very low self esteem. With depression nothing was worth doing and I had become hidden in my home and not doing anything but sitting, sleeping, or staring at the TV. Well, to shorten the story a little I am going to tell you that without the Compeer Quilting Bee I wouldn't have come this far. I look forward to the quilting group each week. I find I really enjoy sharing my knowledge of sewing and serging with anyone who will listen. I have been able to learn a lot about quilting, patience with myself, sharing with others and have gotten a lot of my self-confidence back! I have also been asked to join the Genesee Valley Quilt Club, which I did. I have made many items to sell at our twice a year quilt sale. I have been able to go to the quilt museums with the group, which has gotten me out of the house and interacting with others not only in the quilting groups but our in the community as well. I love that quilting makes me feel as important as anyone else in the group. I love that everyone makes everyone else feel great about themselves and what they accomplish. We all share a common interest and are able to be together every week for several hours. The last but most important thing that has happened to me due to the quilting is that once again I can LAUGH and have fun! I am really glad that Compeer and the quilt group have been there every step of the way. It is so much fun to be able to laugh out loud and not have people stare at you, but join in and laugh too.–Kathleen A.

We will remain dependent on those institutions and individuals who have supported us in the past, but we must continue to be flexible and creative in finding new sources of revenue to meet the needs of the future. We are entrepreneurs at Compeer. We expanded the notion of a non-profit agency, and run Compeer as a business, being ever mindful of new ways to raise the funds and maximize dollars.

Compeer's greatest strength has always been its greatest weakness–the fact that we don't charge for our services. We cannot pass on rising administrative costs to our customers. In order for Compeer to remain a true friendship model based on need and not on the ability to pay, we must rely on the generosity of donors, private and public funding, corporations and governmental agencies.

Volunteer Recruitment

We may succeed in establishing funding sources and creating new services, but the number one challenge we face in running a Compeer program, is finding adequate volunteers. Compeer cannot exist without volunteers; the volunteers drive our services. If we don't have enough volunteers, we can't deliver a successful program or meet our outcome goals.

Again we must be creative. We must look at how we target volunteer recruitment. How do we turn Compeer into an attractive volunteer opportunity, knowing that it is a very challenging one? Compeer is not a showy, glitzy volunteer experience. Compeer is not the place for people who are looking for their name up in lights. Compeer is for people who want to make a difference in other people's lives. We must continuously identify the intrinsic rewards for volunteering at Compeer. What do volunteers gain from the experience? We look for people who have knowledge of or who have been personally touched by mental illness. We want volunteers who believe that they can see the rewards of their time both directly and immediately. Most of all, we look for a caring heart.

We exist in a very competitive environment for volunteers, much more so than when Compeer started thirty years ago. There are so many unmet needs across our country and around the world, and not enough volunteers to tackle these needs. We have to persist in positioning ourselves as a viable choice for volunteers. We must continue to identify and communicate the reasons why a volunteer should choose Compeer instead of other programs. For example, college students can use Compeer as a valuable learning experience.

We must be creative in tapping previously unexplored groups for volunteers. We are increasing our volunteer base of seniors and individuals who have mental and/or physical disabilities to work in our Compeer Calling program.

Compeer continues to utilize print and electronic media regularly, as well as developing new marketing campaigns to promote the value of becoming a Compeer volunteer.

The Stigma Of Mental Illness

Even in the enlightened world of the twenty-first century, the stigma surrounding mental illness continues to present the greatest challenge to Compeer. This stigma inhibits our ability to recruit volunteers. This stigma leads to insufficient governmental, public and other political support. Compeer experiences a setback every time the media runs a story depicting a crime whose perpetrator suffers from a mental illness. That type of news makes the public feel afraid and distrust people who are diagnosed with mental illness. Unfortunately, people who suffer from mental illness do not evoke the same degree of sympathy and compassion as do people with other disabilities.

We are still fighting for parity in insurance coverage for mental health services. We endeavor to have our clients treated and receive the same treatment coverage as do sufferers of any other illness. Due to massive education and advances in treatment, the ignorance of the general public has lessened a bit, but I think society's ideas about and attitudes toward the mentally ill, have not changed as much over the past thirty years as I hoped they would.

The mental health system lacks visible models and sympathetic spokespeople. This results from the reluctance of those who have recovered from mental illness to speak out in public, because they fear they will expose themselves to negative consequences. They are concerned that their frankness will affect their livelihood and concerned about the perceptions their bosses, co-workers, family, and neighbors may have. A diagnosis of mental illness does not sentence one to a life of hopelessness. With proper medication, treatment and support, people who are diagnosed with mental illness can lead healthy, productive lives. We need to have more people speak openly about their mental illness and recovery. They can motivate others to open their hearts and wallets to give current sufferers the support and hope they need.

The Challenge Of A Grass-Roots Organization

The very nature of a grassroots organization means that it responds locally and directly to the changing needs of its community. No one knows the demands and solutions better than the people most immediately affected by them. Compeer Inc. believes that in order for a new Compeer program to meet the needs of its community appropriately, it must be initiated locally, by an individual, a local mental health organization, or a concerned group of citizens. Compeer, Inc. must wait to be contacted by a local group before we can begin to assist them. In an ideal world, we would like to respond to these requests by setting up programs, but we lack the financial and human resources to do this. What we can do is provide the model as well as all the available materials, logos, training manuals, and paper work necessary to set up a flourishing, working Compeer program. We also provide ongoing technical assistance and the know-how garnered from a thirty-year successful track record.

We see an increased demand for Compeer services for a variety of reasons. During these unsettling times we live in, more children and adults will need emotional support. With early detection and treatment, more advances in psychotropic medications, more people will be referred to Compeer. With continued de-emphasis on hospitalization, shrinking dollars of mental health treatment, more demands will be placed on overburdened mental health professionals. Compeer is prepared to grow and meet these challenges.

So much has happened in these thirty years. We have learned many lessons. Compeer has touched thousands of lives. We started with one person's idea, but grew because many people supported us and shared this vision. Compeer depends on the hard work of our Board of Directors and our professional and competent staff. We rely on the championship of the lay leaders of the community who freely share their expertise and time. We exist because of the media who help tell our story, the volunteers who motivate us daily through their acts of kindness, and most of all we thrive because of the clients who do all of the above.

We count on the generosity of donors, both large and small, public and private, individuals, corporations and government, to enable Compeer to remain a true friendship program, based upon need and not upon the ability to pay. We are grateful to the mental health professionals without whose support, belief, recognition, endorsement, and continuing involvement, Compeer would not be a viable adjunct to treatment.

Although Compeer relies on many people and institutions to achieve its goals, it is still true that each individual's contribution is of great and essential significance. Every day our volunteers live out my dream that through the healing power of friendship, one person can indeed make a difference.

27. Bernice Skirboll and Ben Giambrone.

Epilogue: The President's Perspective: From the Corporate Ladder to a Non-Profit Leader

Ben R. Giambrone, President, Compeer, Inc.

Donald Trump once said: "I have made the tough decisions, always with an eye toward the bottom line. Perhaps it's time America was run like a business."

Mr. Trump's quote is an example of how the "run-it-like-a business" phrase is becoming ubiquitous in our society. Politicians often campaign on a platform pledging to run government more like a business. At Compeer, Inc. though, it is more than just a popular saying; it is an integral part of our operations–even more so in light of dwindling government resources and increasing pressure from funding sources to be more efficient and to do more with less.

The perennial goal of running Compeer more like a business was a key factor in the selection of Compeer founder and former president Bernice "Bunny" Skirboll's replacement. After more than three decades in the role, Bernice Skirboll decided to step down as president and to serve the organization in a strategic consulting role. The board of directors turned to me largely because of my corporate management experience.

During the decades Bernice Skirboll was running Compeer's day-to-day operations, I was dedicating my professional life to climbing the corporate ladder–spending more than thirty years in Corporate America. Then in 2004, I took a wonderful detour–stepping off the ladder and entering the non-profit world.

This was not a complete transformation for me, as I had served on several boards of directors and committees for Rochester-area human-service agencies. In fact, I had the opportunity to influence Compeer's strategic direction while serving as chair of Compeer's board of directors for three years prior to taking over as president. My devotion to non-profit organizations was nurtured early on by my parents and family, and it was a natural extension of my deep roots in the Rochester community.

After much discussion with Bernice Skirboll and Compeer board chair Philip Fain, we agreed that the transition from Bernice to me was a logical next step, both for Compeer and for me professionally.

The timing to make such a career change also was right. My wife Pam and I have raised three children—Robb, Charlie, and Catie. Our youngest, Catie, had recently completed college, and Pam and I were looking to get even more involved in the community that we love and in which we chose to raise our family. I assumed the role of Compeer president in the fall of 2004. Pam has since become a Compeer mentor to a youth and an adult. When I retired from my corporate position, I had some concerns about the cultural differences between the two environments. Despite the fact that many businesses develop new products to make our lives better and more convenient, the primary motivation—as bluntly stated by Mr. Trump—is the bottom line: money.

As a regional office leader of a worldwide human-resource benefits company, I worked with employees to help our clients maximize their employee benefits, from health care to retirement, against the backdrop of tremendously growing pressure on resources. I also helped employees set goals and track personal and professional development. I remain extremely proud of what my colleagues and I accomplished together on behalf of our clients. Nevertheless, in the end, the results that mattered most to the corporate hierarchy were the things directly related to company profitability.

That is not to say money isn't important in the non-profit sector, because it is, but for a different reason. While corporations look to increase profits, non-profits constantly worry about where the next dollar is going to come from. We may have devised the best program in the world, but it won't mean anything unless we can find the funding to support it.

It is at this point that the creativity and dedication of the Compeer staff play such a vital role. Compeer's staff members have much responsibility, including identifying potential funding sources, creating and implementing new programs and services, developing creative ways to recruit more volunteers, monitoring the activity of existing volunteers, working with board members, planning and staffing an incredible number of events, and much more.

In the time I have served as Compeer's president, it has not taken very long to recognize and appreciate the tireless dedication of Compeer managers and staff members. Based on my experience, there is no doubt that these well-educated professionals would enjoy much greater earning power in the private sector. Yet they choose to stay at Compeer and continually do amazing work because of a much higher reward—the personal satisfaction they receive from helping people fight the effects of mental illness, such as loneliness and isolation, as well as the stigma associated with mental illness.

I am constantly in awe of how Compeer employees work together for a common cause and of how they celebrate each other's successes. When another child or adult treated for mental illness finds friendship through a Compeer mentor, we all share the success equally and unselfishly. It is truly a team effort and one that I am proud and privileged to help lead.

While governments and other human-service agencies continue to pursue a more business-like operation, Compeer can take pride in the fact that it already has made great strides toward doing just that. Examples include measuring program outcomes, utilizing community resources to enhance operations and tapping into Rochester-area companies for board members and agency partners.

During its more than thirty years of existence, Compeer's mission has remained the same: to bring the power of friendship and mentoring support to children and adults who are being treated for emotional or mental-health issues. Or, as more succinctly stated in our tagline: to make friends and change lives.

Thanks in no small part to Bernice Skirboll's guidance, Compeer managers and staff have always keenly understood the mission and have not taken any action without considering how it will affect that mission. Outside of necessary overhead and administrative costs, each dollar raised goes toward achieving the mission. Each dollar spent is done so only after much deliberation.

I look forward to continuing to build on the model put forth by Bernice Skirboll. She has left an indelible mark on Compeer and on the mental-health field, as evidenced by the story of Compeer's founding and growth and the success stories highlighted throughout this book.

I complement the foundation Bernice helped build by bringing a unique business perspective to the organization, with the goal of helping Compeer continue to become more efficient, to prosper and to expand into even more geographic locations. I am excited to have the opportunity to work side-by-side with my Compeer colleagues, the board of directors and community partners to bring friendship to more people around the world—and to continue making our non-profit agency run like a business.

If we are successful—and I have no doubt that we will be—we will deliver a bottom-line result that is far more valuable than that of any corporation.

The Editors

BERNICE W. SKIRBOLL, the Founder and Executive Consultant of Compeer, earned her Master's degree in Community Services from the University of Rochester. She has received many awards including the Monroe County Medical Society award for dedicated service to the community and to the medical profession, and the United Way Executive Director of the Year award. She was also recognized in the University of Rochester Alumni Directory as one of the most noteworthy alumni who made their mark in the world. Ms. Skirboll's numerous professional presentations include the World Federation of Mental Health Congress, Melbourne, Australia (2003) and the First White House conference on Mental Health (1999). She has served on many boards including the International Association of Psychosocial Rehabilitation Services, and has been a two-time Governor appointee to the New York State National and Community Service Council and a three term Governor appointee to the New York State Mental Health Services Council.

LOIS BENNETT earned an M.A. in Counselor Education from New York University and a J.D. from Boston University School of Law. Her volunteer experience includes work for the Girl Scouts, the Red Cross, an advocacy group for high-risk babies, and many charitable and educational associations. She has also served on the boards of several non-profit organizations including the League of Women Voters.

MARK KLEMENS obtained a Master's degree in Nonprofit Organizations from Case Western Reserve University in Cleveland, Ohio. He has volunteered for a number of organizations, including Contact-Beaver Valley, a telephone helpline in western Pennsylvania.

Index